LIFE SKILLS Reading 2

COMPREHENSION SKILLS

by
CAROL MULLINS

ISBN# 0-87694-172-2 EDI 366

Contents

Introduction

This book is about reading comprehension. That is, it is about more than just reading words. It is about understanding what you read. All through your life, you will have to read and understand many different kinds of reading material. Letters. Directions. Warnings. Newspapers. Legal papers. Forms. Guarantees. Owners' manuals for the things you buy. And so on.

The lessons in this book will give you practice in reading and understanding these different kinds of reading materials. The first half of the book contains many short examples that will allow you to develop your skills. The second half contains longer or more difficult examples that will give you more practice and allow you to improve your reading skills. When you have completed the book, you should have a good basic understanding of how to cope with many of the materials you will be reading throughout your life.

Unit 1
MAIN IDEA

If a piece of writing is more than a few sentences long, it is usually made up of sections called paragraphs. Paragraphs make writing easier to read. Often, a paragraph contains at least one Main Idea that the writing is trying to get across. The rest of the paragraph then contains material that supports the Main Idea. You may not be able to remember everything in the paragraph. But it's not very hard to find and remember the Main Idea.

The lessons in this unit will give you practice in finding and remembering the Main Idea in short paragraphs from many different kinds of Life Skills Reading.

1. HEADINGS AND LISTS

Read the ad below.

Notice that it consists of a **HEADING** (in capitals) and a **LIST** containing 2 items.

from an ADVERTISING LETTER

AT LAST!
***TWO* TYPES OF SERVICE—**
FROM

NATIONAL PARCEL DELIVERY

- **Fast truck delivery of packages**
- **Even faster delivery by airplane and truck—costs only slightly more**

QUESTIONS

1. What is the Main Idea of this ad?
   __ a. National Parcel Delivery has two types of service
   __ b. small packages go on a truck
   __ c. delivery by airplane and truck costs more

2. Where is the Main Idea of this ad?
   __ a. in the heading
   __ b. in the list

from a LABEL

3. Read this panel from a bottle of floor cleaner. What is the Main Idea here?
   __ a. advantages of Shine 'n' Clean
   __ b. don't rinse
   __ c. don't wax

4. Look at items 1-5 in the Shine 'n' Clean label. These are —
   __ a. the Main Idea
   __ b. facts that support the Main Idea

2. TOPIC SENTENCES

Read the notice below.

Notice that one of the sentences tells you the Main Idea of the notice.

This sentence is called a **TOPIC SENTENCE**.

QUESTIONS

1. Which sentence contains the Main Idea of the notice?
   __ a. first sentence
   __ b. second sentence

2. Which sentence gives some examples of the things that must not be left in the hall?
   __ a. first sentence
   __ b. second sentence

3. Which is a topic sentence?
   __ a. first sentence
   __ b. second sentence

4. The topic sentence of the notice contains —
   __ a. the main point that the building super wants to get across
   __ b. the examples that explain what he means

from a POSTER

5. Read this ad from the Blue Angel Cafe.

   Decide which of the three sentences contains the Main Idea. Then underline it.

THE BLUE ANGEL CAFÉ
Sat, Jan 5

MANUEL DEL RIO

Manuel Del Rio is a well-known Mexican musician. He has played in clubs all over the country. His songs are featured by leading Latin groups.

from a MEDICINE BOTTLE LABEL

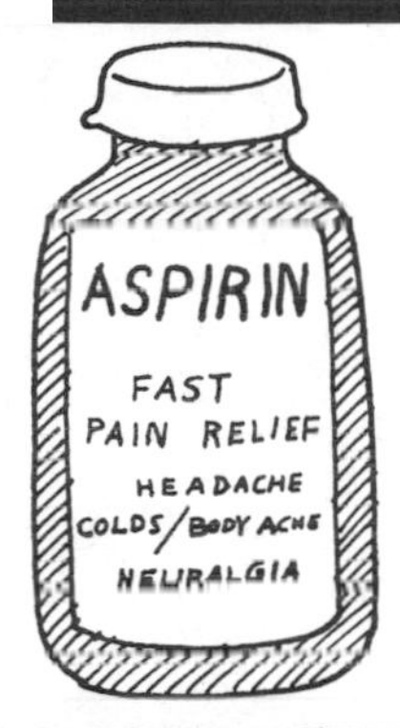

Aspirin reduces fever. It relieves pain. Most people can take it safely. Aspirin is one of the most useful and widely used drugs.

6. A topic sentence contains the Main Idea of a paragraph. It is often the first sentence, but it doesn't have to be.

   Read this paragraph from the label on an aspirin bottle. The topic sentence is not the first sentence.

   Find the topic sentence and underline it.

from a CHILD CARE BOOKLET

7. Read this paragraph from a child care booklet. Find the topic sentence and underline it.

In July last year, a 3-year-old girl died of heat stroke in a closed car. In August, a baby died in the same way. Too many small children have died locked in cars on hot days.

from a VACATION CLUB AD

8. Read this paragraph from a booklet advertising a vacation club. Find the topic sentence and underline it.

When you pay the Holiday Club fee, you will have no other vacation expenses. Your plane trip is paid for. So is your housing and all meals at the Club. All beaches and sports are free.

MAIN IDEA AND SUPPORTING FACTS

A paragraph with a Main Idea contains **SUPPORTING FACTS** as well. These supporting facts may be —

- **details** that fill out the Main Idea
- **reasons** explaining the Main Idea or **reasons** for a request
- **examples** of what the Main Idea is talking about

Read the paragraph below. It is part of a letter from a customer to the company that developed her photographs. Notice both the topic sentence and the supporting facts.

from a LETTER OF COMPLAINT

The photos are all an odd green color. And there are marks from dirt and hairs on them. These photos are not satisfactory.

QUESTIONS

1. Which sentence in the letter contains the Main Idea?
   __ a. Sentence 1
   __ b. Sentence 2
   __ c. Sentence 3

2. Which sentences contain supporting facts? (Check more than one.)
   __ a. Sentence 1
   __ b. Sentence 2
   __ c. Sentence 3

3. Which tells why the customer thinks the photographs are not satisfactory?
   __ a. Main Idea
   __ b. supporting facts

from a BOOK ON ELECTRICAL WIRING

4. Read this paragraph from a book on electrical wiring. Then underline the topic sentence.

5. How many supporting facts are there?
   __ 1 __ 2 __ 3 __ 4 __ 5

6. Copy the supporting facts:
   Fact 1: ______________________________
   Fact 2: ______________________________
   Fact 3: ______________________________

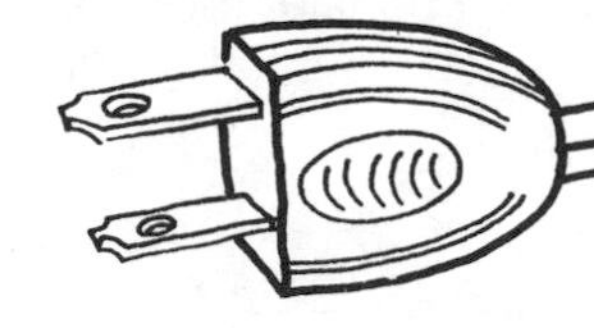

Bare or damaged electrical wires are dangerous. They can start fires. They can shock someone. They can damage appliances.

from a TV MOVIE REVIEW

1AM (2) MOVIE—Abominable Snowman (1983)

Contains some of the finest special effects ever filmed. This is one reason "Abominable Snowman" deserves to be considered the year's best thriller. Another reason is the fine acting of Erik Lumpe as the Snowman.

7. Read this paragraph from a TV movie review. Then underline the Main Idea.

8. Circle the sentence that contains the first supporting idea.

9. Put a check mark at the beginning of the sentence that contains the second supporting idea.

from a CAR OWNER'S MANUAL

10. Not everything in a paragraph is a topic sentence or a supporting fact. Sometimes a sentence just repeats the Main Idea.

    Read the paragraph from the car owner's manual. Underline the sentence that just repeats the Main Idea.

Change your motor oil as often as every 5,000 miles. Motor oil can look clean and still be too old. Old motor oil can damage your engine. So be sure to change your motor oil before it's too late.

4. MAIN IDEA WITH NO TOPIC SENTENCE

Read the following paragraph carefully. Then answer the questions about it below.

from a SUPERMARKET NEWSLETTER

Chicken prices are up because of last summer's heat. Pork and beef are higher, but not as much. Fruits and vegetables are always higher at this time of year.

QUESTIONS

1. Something is missing from this paragraph. What is it?
   __ a. a topic sentence
   __ b. supporting facts

2. Although the paragraph above has no topic sentence, it does have a Main Idea. How would you find it?
   __ a. summarize the paragraph
   __ b. use one of its sentences

3. The following is not a good Main Idea for the paragraph:
   MEAT PRICES ARE HIGHER.
   Why not?
   __ a. it is too short
   __ b. it isn't correct
   __ c. it summarizes only part of the paragraph

4. Which is the best statement of the Main Idea in the paragraph?
   __ a. fruit prices are higher
   __ b. food prices are higher
   __ c. all prices are higher

4. Main Idea with No Topic Sentence

from a CATALOG AD

Having a party? A disco night at your school or club? Try one of our mirror balls to make bits of light dance around the room. Or try our black lights to make white clothes glow. Or walk on a cloud with one of our cloud machines.

5. Read this ad. It has no topic sentence. Think about what the company wants you to remember after you read the ad.

   What is the best statement of the Main Idea for the paragraph?

   __ a. black lights make white clothes glow

   __ b. we have lots of great special effects for parties and discos

   __ c. you should give lots of parties

from a HIGHWAY SAFETY BOOKLET

6. Read this paragraph from a booklet on highway safety.

   What is the best statement of the Main Idea of the paragraph?

   __ a. here's what to do if you are in your car when a storm comes

   __ b. lightning and tornadoes don't come together

   __ c. stay in your car if a storm approaches

A car is a fairly safe place to be during a lightning storm. But if a tornado is headed your way, you may be safer outside your car.

from an OWNER'S MANUAL

The record and playback heads of a tape player should be cleaned every 30 days or so. The tape guides should be cleaned at the same time. So should the rollers and other parts that move the tape through your machine.

7. Read this paragraph from a fix-it-yourself booklet.

   What is the Main Idea of the paragraph?

   __ a. clean the tape recorder once a month

   __ b. rollers and other parts move the tape

   __ c. the record and playback heads need cleaning

UNIT 1 REVIEW

from a JOB DESCRIPTION

1. What is the Main Idea?
   __ a. requirements for employment
   __ b. state license as electrician
   __ c. four years experience as electrician in home-building industry

REQUIREMENTS FOR EMPLOYMENT

1. State license as electrician

2. Four years experience as electrician in home-building industry

2. In a list with a heading, the Main Idea is usually found —
   __ a. in the heading
   __ b. in the list

from an ADVERTISING LETTER

3. Underline the Main Idea in the paragraph at the right.

Is your package going to someone high in a city office building? Or to a house in the suburbs? Or to a ranch far from the beaten track? We give door-to-door service anywhere in the country.

from a SEED CATALOG

4. Read this paragraph from a seed catalog. Then look at the two lists with headings below.
   Check the list that has the same Main Idea and supporting points that the paragraph does.

Spacesaver seeds grow lots of cucumbers. And Spacesaver vines take up only 1/3 the space of regular cucumber vines. Spacesaver cucumbers are ideal for the small garden.

__ A.

SPACESAVER CUCUMBERS ARE IDEAL FOR THE SMALL GARDEN
1. Spacesaver seeds grow lots of cucumbers.
2. Spacesaver vines take up only 1/3 the space of regular cucumber vines.

__ B.

SPACESAVER SEEDS GROW LOTS OF CUCUMBERS
1. Spacesaver vines take up only 1/3 the space of regular cucumber vines.
2. Spacesaver cucumbers are ideal for the small garden.

from an ANTI-SMOKING BOOKLET

5. Read this paragraph from an anti-smoking booklet. Which is the Main Idea of the paragraph?
   __ a. a half day after you quit, you're on your way to better health
   __ b. the heart and lungs begin to repair smoke damage
   __ c. the level of nicotine goes down fast

Within 12 hours after a person quits smoking, he or she is on the way to better health. The level of nicotine (a poisonous chemical in tobacco) goes down fast. The heart and lungs begin to repair smoke damage.

from a LETTER ASKING FOR MONEY

Dear Friend:

In many parts of Africa, almost every child under 5 is unhealthy because of poor diet. More than half of all childhood deaths in Latin America are related to not getting enough to eat. And in India, 75% of pre-school children do not get enough to eat.

6. Read this paragraph from a letter asking you to give money. Does it have a topic sentence?
   __ yes __ no

7. Which is the best statement of the Main Idea?
   __ a. children
   __ b. many African children do not get enough to eat
   __ c. many children in the world do not get enough to eat

Unit 2
DIRECTIONS

Directions are a very important kind of Life Skills Reading. You have to pay very close attention when you are reading them. If you don't understand a newspaper article, it may not really make much difference to you. But if you read a direction wrong, whatever you are trying to do will almost certainly go wrong also.

This unit will give you training and practice in reading and following many different kinds of directions.

5. BASIC DIRECTIONS

The simplest kind of direction tells you, straight out to do something or not to do it. Other kinds of directions are less direct. At first, they may not even look like directions. You must read carefully to recognize that they are really telling you to do something.

For an example, read the note below.

from a MEMO FROM A BOSS

Bill—
Find out how much we promised to pay Moody Electrical Supply Co. The information is in the "Lighting" file.
Thanks.

WORDS AND MEANINGS

If you find some words you do not understand in this lesson, look them up in this section.

ingest — eat or drink

guarantee — promise to fix or replace something that you buy if it does not work

insure — buy insurance so that if something is broken or lost, the insurance company will pay for it

QUESTIONS

1. Look back at the note, above. Which sentence in the note tells you straight out to do something?
   __ a. Sentence 1
   __ b. Sentence 2

2. The second sentence in the note is really a kind of direction, too. It means —
   __ a. pay Moody Electrical from the "Lighting" file.
   __ b. look up the information in the "Lighting" file.
   __ c. put the information in the "Lighting" file

from a BOTTLE LABEL

3. The next question will be about a label that contains the word ingest. Suppose you don't know what ingest means. What did the directions above say to do?
   __ a. make a guess
   __ b. look up the word in the "Words and Meanings" section

4. Suppose you had a bottle that says, "Do not ingest" on the label. What should you do?
   __ a. eat the contents
   __ b. drink the contents
   __ c. do not eat or drink the contents

5. Directions are often not as direct as "Find It!" or "Do not open."

   What does it really mean if someone says, "You should sit over there"?

   __ a. that is a chair

   __ b. sit over there

6. What is another way of saying, "Do not wear this while swimming"?

   __ a. not to be worn while swimming

   __ b. no swimming

7. Which sentence below is really a direction? Check it.

   __ a. It would be helpful if you would write as soon as possible.

   __ b. The building plans will be ready as soon as possible.

8. Which sentence below is really a direction?

   __ a. The city takes in $26,000 a year from its parking meters.

   __ b. The law requires you to put 25 cents in the parking meter for every hour you park.

from a WATCH GUARANTEE

9. Read this paragraph from a watch guarantee.

   > *The guarantee on your watch does not cover anything that happens in the mail. We suggest that you insure your watch if you mail it.*

   Which sentence is the direction?

   __ a. Sentence 1

   __ b. Sentence 2

6. STEP-BY-STEP DIRECTIONS

Many directions have several steps. When you run across directions like these, it is important to follow them in the correct order.

Read the directions on the bottle of rubber cement, below.

from DIRECTIONS ON A BOTTLE OF RUBBER CEMENT

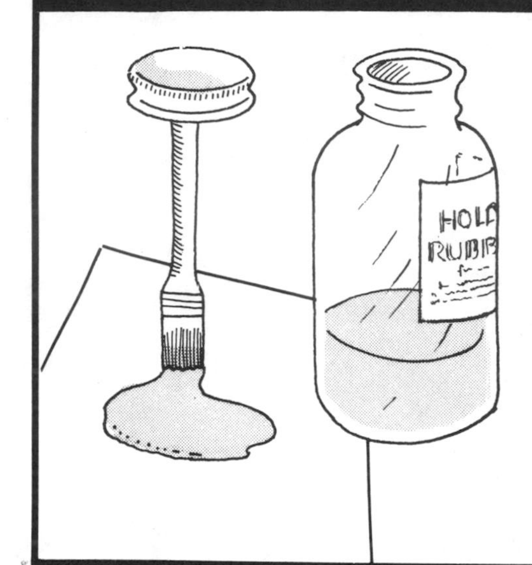

HOLD-IT RUBBER CEMENT

for work with paper

DIRECTIONS

1. **Brush onto *one* surface**
2. **Press into place**
3. **When dry, rub off excess with eraser**

WORDS AND MEANINGS

excess — an extra amount you don't need

preheat — heat before you start to cook

griddle — a flat metal pan without sides. Use a regular frying pan if you don't have one.

liquid — something that flows. Water, oil, and milk are liquids.

batter — a mixture containing flour and a liquid, used in making pancakes

evaporating — drying up

shortening — fat used in cooking, like butter, margarine, or oil

QUESTIONS

1. Brian is pasting pictures into a scrapbook with rubber cement. What should he do first?

   __ a. brush the cement onto a picture

   __ b. brush cement onto both the picture and a scrapbook page

   __ c. press a picture in place

2. What should Brian do after he presses the picture in place?

   __ a. clean off extra cement

   __ b. clean the brush

   __ c. dry the bottle

3. When should he do this?

   __ a. as soon as the picture is in place

   __ b. after the cement is dry

4. How should he do this?

   __ a. with a brush

   __ b. with an eraser

   __ c. with a knife

from a LABEL ON A BOX OF PANCAKE MIX

Read the directions for making pancakes. Then answer Questions 5-10.

FOR PANCAKES

Preheat griddle. Note: Griddle is ready when a small drop of water dances on it before evaporating.

Place mix, milk, egg and melted or liquid shortening in bowl.

Stir until batter is fairly smooth.

Pour batter onto hot, lightly greased griddle. Turn pancakes when tops are covered with bubbles and edges look cooked. Turn only once.

5. How can you be sure the pan is hot enough before you pour in the batter?
   __ a. see if a drop of water jumps around before it disappears
   __ b. test it with your finger
   __ c. check it with a thermometer

6. Many people use salad oil for shortening. If you want to use butter, what must you do to it?
   __ a. freeze it
   __ b. mash it
   __ c. melt it

7. When should you stir the batter?
   __ a. after you pour it on the griddle
   __ b. before you pour it on the griddle
   __ c. as you pour it on the griddle

8. When should you stop stirring the batter?
   __ a. when it is completely smooth with absolutely no lumps at all
   __ b. when it is mostly smooth with only a few small lumps
   __ c. when it is very lumpy

9. When can you turn the pancakes over?
   __ a. it does not matter
   __ b. the top must have bubbles and the edges must look done
   __ c. the top must look brown

10. How often should you turn the pancakes over?
   __ a. as often as needed
   __ b. once
   __ c. two or three times

7. DIRECTIONS WITH PICTURES

Many directions come with pictures. The step-by-step directions in "How-to" books often come with pictures, for example. Pictures make it easier to see what the directions are talking about.

Read the step-by-step directions below. They are from a booklet on home repairs.

Notice how the pictures help explain each step. Notice also how the directions refer to the pictures by using the abbreviation "Fig." The abbreviation "Fig." stands for "Figure" — another way of saying "picture."

from a GOVERNMENT BOOKLET ON HOME REPAIR

HOW TO REPLACE A BROKEN WINDOW

1. Work from outside the window frame. This usually means outside the house. (Fig. 1)
2. Use pliers to pull out the broken glass. (Fig. 2)
3. Use a chisel to clean away old putty. Then pull out old glazier's points with pliers (Fig. 3)
4. Run a thin ribbon of putty all around the frame. (Fig. 4)
5. Press the correct size pane of glass firmly against the putty. (Fig. 5)
6. Carefully tap in new glazier's points all around the frame, 4 to 6 inches apart. Do the corners first. (Fig. 6)
7. Run another ribbon of putty all around the window so that it covers the glazier's points. Use a putty knife or your fingers to press the putty against the window and to make a smooth seal all around. (Fig. 7.)

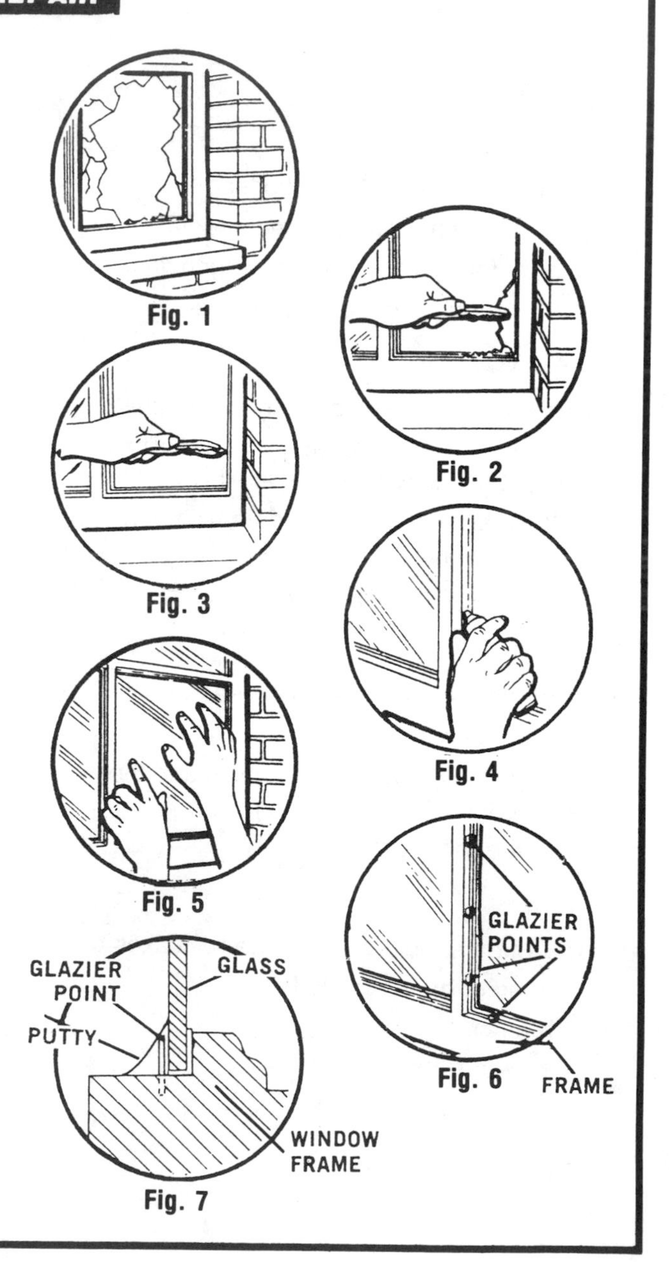

WORDS AND MEANINGS

pliers — this tool: 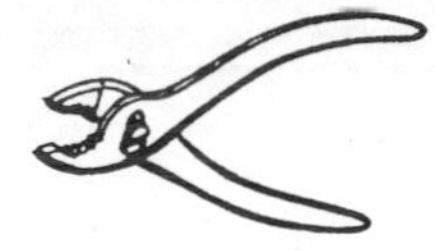

glazier — person who puts glass in windows

glazier's points — small metal triangles that hold glass in place

putty — a kind of dough-like cement for holding glass in place and filling holes

seal — something that closes something else completely

putty knife — a metal blade to push putty in place

QUESTIONS

1. Where do you have to be while fixing a window?
   __ a. inside the window
   __ b. outside the window

2. What must you do just before putting the new glass in the frame?
   __ a. place a little putty all around the frame
   __ b. place a little putty all around the outside of the glass
   c. put in the new glazier's points

3. Does the old putty need to be scraped out before putting in new putty?
   __ yes __ no

4. How many times do you put putty all around the window?
   __ a. once
   __ b. twice
   __ c. three or four times

5. What does Fig. 6 help you understand?
   __ a. where to put the putty
   __ b. where to put in the glazier's points

6. Look at Fig. 7. Does the putty cover up the glazier's points?
   __ yes __ no

7. Where should you put the putty in the last step?
   __ a. all around the edge of the window
   __ b. some every 4 to 6 inches

8. How many glazier's points should you put in?
   __ a. as many as you can
   __ b. one every 4 to 6 inches
   c. one for each side

8. CHOOSING WHICH DIRECTION TO FOLLOW

Read the directions below.

Notice that there are three different sets of directions. You must choose which one to follow.

from DIRECTIONS ON A PACKAGE OF FLOUR

For regular size (10-inch) cake, bake about fifty minutes.

For layers of layer cake (8-by-8 inch layers), bake about forty minutes.

For cupcakes, bake about thirty minutes.

QUESTIONS

1. What should you do if you are making a layer cake?
   __ a. bake 50 minutes
   __ b. bake 40 minutes
   __ c. bake 30 minutes

2. How do you follow the directions above?
   __ a. choose only one
   __ b. follow all 3, in order

from a TELEPHONE DIRECTORY

3. Read the instructions at the right. They are from a Telephone Directory (telephone book).

   Mitch wants to call his parents long distance. He wants them to pay for the call. Their Area Code is 606. That is a number that takes the call to their part of Kentucky. Their number is 673-2138.

   What should he dial?
   __ a. 0-606-673-2138
   __ b. 1-606-673-2138
   __ c. 606-673-2138

LONG DISTANCE CALLS

If you want the call charged to the number you are calling from, dial

1 + AREA CODE + TELEPHONE NUMBER

If you want the call charged to the number you are calling, dial

0 + AREA CODE + TELEPHONE NUMBER

9. THE WORD *IF*

Some directions come with the word "if" in them. This word tells you to follow the directions only when whatever follows the word "if" actually happens.

"If" directions are not really tricky. But sometimes people don't notice the word "if" in a set of directions. And they get the directions wrong.

Read the notice below. It is over the door of a car on a subway train.

from a NOTICE IN THE SUBWAY

NOTICE

SUBWAY TRACKS ARE DANGEROUS. DO NOT GET OUT IF THE TRAIN STOPS BETWEEN STATIONS.

QUESTIONS

1. Circle the word "if" in the subway notice.

2. The train stops in a station where you want to get off. What should you do?

   __ a. stay on

   __ b. get off

3. The train stops between stations. It looks like it might be a long wait. What should you do?

   __ a. stay on

   __ b. get off

from a LIST OF OFFICE RULES

RULE 9

Call the office by 9:00 if you are going to be late to work.

4. Read this office rule.

   Do you have to call the office if you are going to be on time?

   __ yes __ no

5. When do you have to call the office by 9:00?

   __ a. every morning

   __ b. only once in a while when something is making you late

6. Does the rule tell you to be late to work?

   __ yes __ no

10. WORDS THAT MEAN NO OR NOT

The words no and not are often used in directions. For example, **NO EXIT. DO NOT ENTER.**

There are many other words used in directions that have the idea of no or not in their meaning. This lesson will give you practice in recognizing them.

Read the paragraph below. It is from the directions for a contest that a supermarket chain is sponsoring. Notice that each underlined word has not in its meaning. If you are not sure of any meaning, look it up in the Words and Meanings section.

from a set of CONTEST DIRECTIONS

WIN A TRIP TO JAMAICA!

ALL EXPENSES PAID! 2 WEEKS!

This contest is open to all U.S. residents except employees of Sullivan's Supermarkets and their families. VOID where prohibited by law.

WORDS AND MEANINGS

U.S. residents — people living in the United States

void — no good

prohibited — not allowed

aching — feeling a dull pain, usually in the muscles, belly, or head

side effects — any effects of taking a medication that are not part of the cure. Sleepiness is a side effect of some cold medicines.

cancel—to remove or stop something. When a business cancels an order, it stops the order from being sent.

QUESTIONS

1. Who is not allowed to enter this contest? (Check one or more.)
   __ a. Anton Slezak. His father is a butcher at Sullivan's
   __ b. Brendan Clark. He shops frequently at Sullivan's
   __ c. Joao Oliveira. He is visiting the U.S. from Brazil

2. Who is allowed to enter the contest? (Check one or more.)
   __ a. Nelli Fong. Her state prohibits contests like this one
   __ b. Reba Jackson. She works as a checkout clerk at Sullivan's
   __ c. Vangie Duparc. She went to Jamaica two years ago

from a COUPON

3. A 10-cents-off coupon in a package of garbage bags says, "Offer void after May 15." Check each date that the offer is good.
   __ a. March 29
   __ b. April 7
   __ c. May 23

4. A sign in a bus says, "Smoking prohibited." This means —
   __ a. smoking allowed
   __ b. smoking permitted
   __ c. no smoking

from a MEDICINE BOTTLE LABEL

5. Words that start with <u>dis</u>- or <u>un</u>- often have <u>not</u> in their meaning.

   Read the label on the bottle of medicine at the right.

   Fred DiMello gets a bad rash whenever he takes this medicine. What does the label tell him to do?
   __ a. call a doctor
   __ b. continue using it more often
   __ c. stop taking the medicine

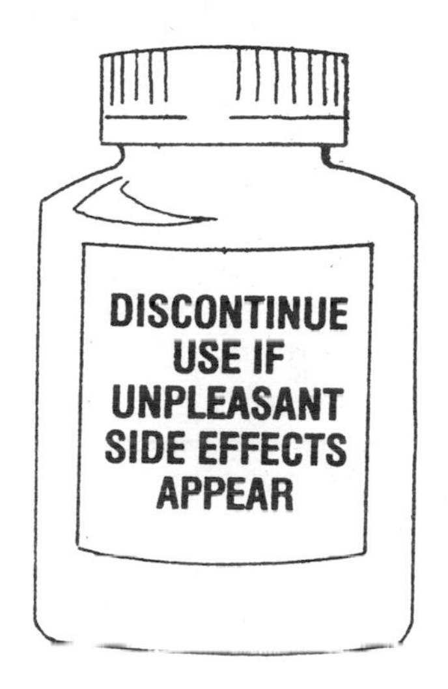

6. A medicine label says, "for discomfort caused by colds." Which of the following feelings is the label talking about? (Check one or more.)
   __ a. aching muscles
   __ b. pleasant, sleepy feeling
   __ c. uncomfortable stuffy feeling

from a RECORD CLUB NOTICE

A NOTE of REMINDER

JUST TO REMIND OUR MEMBERS HOW THE SOCIETY OPERATES

We will send you this month's selection of records by August 15 unless we receive your request to cancel shipment by August 1.

7. Read this notice from a record club.

   Renee Haupt belongs to this record club. She doesn't want the records that are offered for August. What should she do?
   __ a. she should notify the record club after August 15
   __ b. she should notify the record club before August 1
   __ c. she doesn't have to do anything

11. WARNINGS

Warnings are, in effect, a kind of direction.

By telling you about something bad that can happen if you do something, they tell you not to do it.

Read the underlined warning below from the directions on a box of pancake mix. Notice that the warning does not come right out and tell you not to do something. But it doesn't really need to. You can figure it out.

from a COOKBOOK RECIPE

For light pancakes, mix batter only until fairly smooth. Overmixing makes pancakes thin and tough.

WORDS AND MEANINGS

qualifications — experiences or training that prepare a person for a job

exaggerated — stretching the truth

misstatement — an untruth or a lie

disqualification — saying a person cannot get a job

QUESTIONS

1. What should you do if you want light pancakes?
   __ a. keep mixing the batter until it is completely smooth
   __ b. mix only until fairly smooth

2. What should you do if you want thin, tough pancakes?
   __ a. mix batter completely
   __ b. mix only until fairly smooth

3. Which sounds the best?
   __ a. light, tender pancakes
   __ b. thin, tough pancakes

4. The warning is a direction that means —
   __ a. mix batter until completely smooth
   __ b. do not mix batter until completely smooth

from a GOVERNMENT BOOKLET ON STAIN REMOVAL

Many stains are easy to remove if they are treated right away. But they may never come out if you wait too long to treat them.

5. Read this warning from a government booklet on getting stains out of cloth.

   Simon's pen leaked in his shirt pocket. What may happen if he waits several days to get the ink stain out?

   __ a. it will become easier to remove

   __ b. it will become harder to remove

   __ c. it will fade by itself

6. The warning is actually a direction that means —

   __ a. do not treat stains

   __ b. take your time before you treat stains

   __ c. treat stains right away if you can

7. The warning on a bottle of bleach says:

   MAY CAUSE BLINDNESS

   This warning is really a direction that means —

   __ a. don't get bleach in your eyes

   __ b. don't use too much bleach in the laundry

from a JOB APPLICATION FORM

8. Owen wants to get a job as a carpenter. On his job application form is a paragraph that says:

   WE WILL CHECK ON YOUR STATEMENTS OF QUALIFICATIONS. MISSTATEMENTS OR EXAGGERATION ARE REASONS FOR DISQUALIFICATION.

   This warning is a direction that means —

   __ a. don't check on your statements

   __ b. don't check on your misstatements

   __ c. don't lie or stretch the truth

9. Owen is really a good carpenter, but on his last job he was a sweeper in the carpentry shop. He was allowed to cut boards only once.

   If Owen wrote "ran the table saw" when he describes his last job, what does the warning say the employer will do?

   __ a. hire him right away

   __ b. check on his statement, and hire him because he did run a table saw at least once

   __ c. check on his statement and not hire him because he exaggerated

UNIT 2 REVIEW

from DIRECTIONS ON A TAX FORM

1. Read the paragraph at the right.
   Who must send in copies of the form?
   __ a. everyone
   __ b. every tax payer
   __ c. only people starting their own business

If you are starting your own business, you must make out 3 copies of the License Application Form 308-C and send them to the Department of Taxation.

from a BOOKLET ON HOME CARE

2. Read the paragraphs at the right.
   Rust is very hard to get out. A bathtub ring is easy to get out. Which method should you use for rust?
   __ a. make a paste with the cleanser and let it stand before rubbing it
   __ b. sprinkle on the cleanser and clean immediately with a damp sponge

FOR ORDINARY CLEANING:
Sprinkle on cleanser, clean with a damp sponge and rinse.
FOR EXTRA TOUGH STAINS
Wet surface, sprinkle on cleanser, rub lightly to make a paste, wait one minute, rub hard, then rinse.

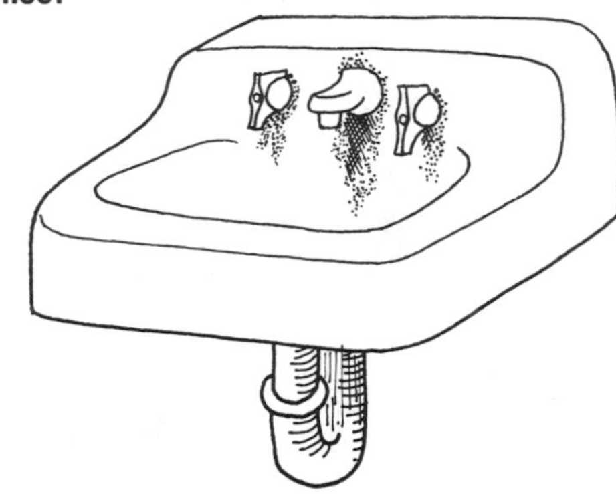

from an AD ON GASOLINE CONSERVATION

3. Read this paragraph.
   What happens when you idle the motor?
   __ a. you get good use of gasoline
   __ b. you waste gasoline

Idling the motor is running it without moving the car. Idling wastes gasoline and gets 0 miles to the gallon.

4. What should you do?
   __ a. idle the motor
   __ b. not idle the motor

5. Look again at the paragraphs on this page.
   Which one contains a warning?
   __ a. the paragraph with Question 1
   __ b. the paragraphs with Question 2
   __ c. the paragraph with Question 3 and 4

from a COMPANY INSURANCE BOOKLET

6. Underline the direction in the paragraph at the right.

The law states that you must tell your employer immediately any time you are hurt at work. This is to protect your rights to free medical care.

from a CAR OWNER'S MANUAL

7. Read the paragraph at the right.
   What is the first step in checking the oil?
   __ a. reading the dipstick
   __ b. starting the motor
   __ c. turning off the motor

8. How does Fig. 1 help you understand Step 2?
   __ a. shows where to find the dipstick
   __ b. shows how to turn off the motor
   __ c. shows how to read the dipstick

9. After you take the dipstick out for the first time, what is the next thing to do with it?
   __ a. clean the oil off it
   __ b. read it
   __ c. put it back

10. Look at the oil level on the dipstick. How much oil do you need to add?
    __ a. none
    __ b. 1 quart
    __ c. 2 quarts

11. After you read the oil level on the dipstick, what should you do with the dipstick?
    __ a. clean oil off it
    __ b. put it back
    __ c. throw it away

TO CHECK IF YOUR CAR NEEDS OIL:

1. **Turn off motor**
2. **Take out dipstick (see Fig. 1)**
3. **Clean dipstick**
4. **Replace dipstick**
5. **Take out dipstick**
6. **Read oil level on dipstick (see Fig. 2)**
7. **Replace dipstick**

Fig. 1

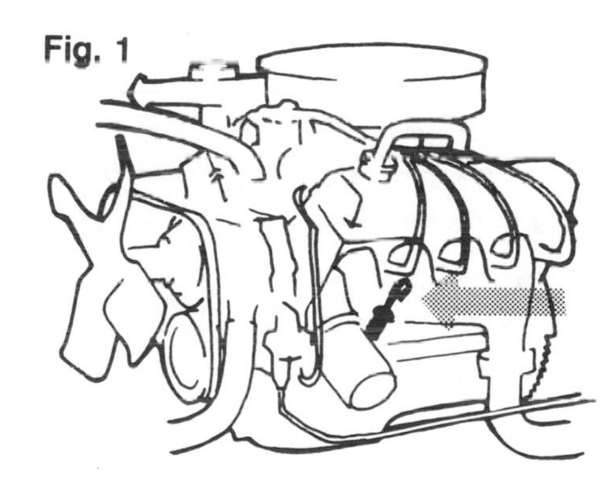

Fig. 2

Oil level can be below this level and still be safe

If oil level is below this level add 1 quart of oil

If oil level is below this level add 2 quarts of oil

FULL

ADD

Unit 3
UNFAMILIAR WORDS

What do you do if you are reading something, and you come upon a word you don't understand?

You can, of course, look it up in the dictionary. Often that's the only way to find out what the word means, unless you ask someone who already knows. But there are other ways you can use that let you make a good guess at the meaning. This unit will teach you two of these ways.

12. WORD MEANINGS FROM EXAMPLES

Read the notice from the paint can label below.

Notice the word masonry, and the examples of what the word means.

Try to guess what the word means from the examples. See if you can think of other examples of masonry, too.

QUESTIONS

1. Which is an example of masonry?
   __ a. a brick wall
   __ b. a wooden table
   __ c. wallpaper

2. What is masonry?
   __ a. something built of stone or a material like stone
   __ b. any kind of a wall
   __ c. wood or metal

3. Which of the following is an example of masonry?
   __ a. a cement sidewalk
   __ b. aluminum siding
   __ c. a plastic window frame

4. Check the item that you cannot paint with Laurel Paint.
   __ a. a cinder block shed
   __ b. a plaster wall
   __ c. a floor with wax on it

from a PACKAGE LABEL

5. Read the notice on the bean package at the right. Notice the words foreign substances.
   Find and underline any examples of foreign substances in the notice.

6. Which is a foreign substance in this package?
   __ a. a large bean
   __ b. a small stone
   __ c. a Dutch pot

7. The abbreviation etc. tells you that there are other examples of foreign substances besides the ones listed on the label. Do you think a piece of plastic would be a foreign substance?
   __ yes __ no

8. The word foreign substance on a package label refers to —
   __ a. the package itself
   __ b. the contents of the package
   __ c. anything that doesn't belong in the package

DUTCH POT
DRIED LIMA BEANS

Please Note

This product comes from the earth. Please look at the contents carefully. Sort out any foreign substances (twigs, small stones, pieces of soil, etc.) Rinse beans well before cooking.

9. What would be a foreign substance in a can of vegetable soup?
   __ a. peas
   __ b. carrots
   __ c. mouse hairs

from a GUARANTEE ON A WASHING MACHINE

10. Read this paragraph from a washing machine guarantee at the right. Notice the words consequential damages.
    Find examples of consequential damages on the guarantee and underline them.

11. What are consequential damages?
    __ a. outside problems caused by the broken washing machine
    __ b. broken parts or other things wrong with the washing machine itself

12. George's washing machine overflowed and ruined the apartment downstairs. What will the guarantee cover?
    __ a. fixing the broken washing machine
    __ b. fixing the mess in the apartment downstairs
    __ c. both of the above

GUARANTEE

This guarantee promises only to pay for repairs to the washing machine itself. It does NOT cover consequential damages, such as torn clothing or flooded floors.

17. WORD MEANINGS FROM CONTEXT CLUES

Read the paragraph below.

Notice the underlined word.

Also notice the words that are circled. Use these words to help figure out the meaning of the underlined word. These helpful words are called the **CONTEXT.**

QUESTIONS

1. What do the context words tell you about the word attire?
   __ a. you cook it
   __ b. you dress in it
   __ c. it is a type of photo

2. What is your attire?
   __ a. how you feel about things
   __ b. your clothes
   __ c. your job identification

3. What should employees wear for their photos?
   __ a. anything
   __ b. their best clothes
   __ c. their regular clothes for going to work

4. What is context?
   __ a. any difficult word
   __ b. nearby words that help you understand a difficult word
   __ c. something to wear

from a NEWSPAPER AD

5. The word receipt has more than one meaning. You need to notice the context to choose the right meaning.

   Read this section from a newspaper ad. What does receipt mean in these sentences?

   __ a. a paper showing in writing how much was paid for something

   __ b. receiving or getting something

> Send in your request right away. It takes 10 days from receipt of your request until the catalog is sent.

from a GIFT CATALOG

HIDE YOUR MONEY IN THIS BOOK SAFE

A thief needs x-ray vision to discern what is inside this book. On a shelf with other books it will be so inconspicuous that even you might have trouble finding it! The cavity is 8" long, 5" wide, 1" deep.

NB271 Booksafe $15.00

6. Read the paragraph above. Use the context and the picture to figure out the meanings of the underlined words.

   What is a book-safe?

   __ a. a book safe for children to read

   __ b. a fake book with a space for hiding things

7. What does discern mean?

   __ a. blink

   __ b. hide

   __ c. see

8. Something that is inconspicuous is —

   __ a. easy to notice

   __ b. hard to notice

9. What is a cavity?

   __ a. a hole or a space inside something

   __ b. a kind of jewel

   __ c. x-ray eyes

10. The numbers in the last line of the book-safe ad have little marks after them. The marks look like this: ". What do they mean in this ad?

    __ a. the same thing

    __ b. inches

    __ c. yes or no

UNIT 3 REVIEW

1. A government job application form contains a paragraph that says,

   You must complete the entire application form. Do not send a resume in lieu of completing this statement.

   What do you think the words in lieu of mean?

   __ a. because of
   __ b. instead of
   __ c. during

2. A safety notice sent by a gas company to its customers says,

   The U.S. Consumer Products Safety Commission has informed us that some types of connectors used to connect appliances to gas lines may have deteriorated with time and become dangerously defective. Gas may leak through these deteriorated connectors.

   What do you think the word deteriorated means?

   __ a. improved
   __ b. gone bad
   __ c. replaced

3. A warning notice on a package of medicine says,

   Reduce dosage or stop using this medication if such symptoms as coughing, headaches, restlessness, sleeplessness, or rapid heartbeat occur.

   What do you think the word symptoms means?

   __ a. doctors and nurses
   __ b. medicines that cause coughing, headaches, etc.
   __ c. signs that something is going wrong in your body

4. A consumer's handbook says,

   Many banks have a wide variety of consumer services, including checking accounts, consumer loans, savings accounts, and help with many other kinds of financial transactions.

   What do you think financial transactions are?

   __ a. deals involving money
   __ b. government departments
   __ c. sickness or illness

5. An ad for "ice walkers" in a catalog says,

   Pull on a pair of these ice walkers over your shoes and walk over any icy surface! Six special, long-wearing spikes give traction on the ice just like a snow tire with metal studs.

   What do you think the word traction means?

   __ a. footprints or tracks
   __ b. a grip on a slippery surface
   __ c. hard metal that won't wear away easily

6. A notice from an electric company reads,

   We have not been able to get into your apartment to read your meter for several months. We will have to add a $25 charge to your bill for not providing access...We will not, however, add the charge at this time if someone will be home on Wednesday, July 7, to let our meter reader in.

   What do you think the words providing access mean?

   __ a. keeping someone out
   __ b. letting someone in
   __ c. reading an electric meter

Unit 4
GETTING THE DETAILS STRAIGHT

In the first unit of this Skillbook, you learned how to spot the main idea of a paragraph. But often you will also need to sort out and remember the important facts and details in what you are reading.

This unit will help you learn a way to spot those important facts and details, to understand them, and to remember them longer. The trick is to ask yourself seven questions as you read, and to spot the answers in what you are reading.

The seven questions are—

WHO? (Who is it about?)

WHAT? (What is it about? or What's happening?)

WHY? (Why is it happening?)

WHEN? (When—past, present, or future)

WHERE? (Where is it happening?)

HOW? (How is it happening? or How is it being done?)

WHICH ONE? (When more than one thing is being talked about)

This unit will show you, step by step, how to use these seven questions to improve your reading skills.

14. WHAT'S HAPPENING AND WHY

Read the 3 sentences below. They are from different parts of a bus company circular. For each of them ask yourself two questions:

- **WHAT** is going to happen?
- **WHY?**

from a BUS COMPANY CIRCULAR

1. **The effect of the bus drivers' raise will be a fare increase.**
2. **Bus fares will increase because the drivers just got a raise.**
3. **Bus fares will go up 25 cents.**

QUESTIONS

1. All three sentences say that the bus fare is going up.
   Read Sentence 1 and ask yourself **WHY**. Choose the best answer below.
   __ a. the bus drivers got a raise
   __ b. the company just wanted more money
   __ c. no one knows

2. What is the answer to **WHY** in Sentence 2?
   __ a. can't tell, not enough information
   __ b. same as the reason given in Sentence 1

3. What is the answer to **WHY** in Sentence 3?
   __ a. there is not enough information
   __ b. same as in Sentence 1
   __ c. 25 cents

4. Words like reason, cause, because, and effect often help you find answers to **WHY** questions.
   Underline any of these words in the three sentences above.

5. Sentences without words like because and reason can still give facts about why something is happening.
   Which sentence at the right has information about **WHY**?
   __ a. Sentence 1
   __ b. Sentence 2

6. Which word in the sentence tells you that the question **WHY** will be answered?
   __ a. easily
   __ b. since
   __ c. usually

1	*Since meat spoils easily, it is usually kept in the refrigerator.*
2	*Most people keep meat in the refrigerator or the freezer.*

15. WHO, WHAT, AND WHY

Read the paragraph below. It is from the TV section of a newspaper.

Notice the **WHO, WHAT,** and **WHY** questions below the TV review. Ask yourself these questions as you read.

from a TV LISTING IN A NEWSPAPER

10:30

(4) CAVEMAN 2000. A bumbling gumshoe masquerades as a caveman to trap a mad scientist bent on world domination.

WHO is it about?

WHAT did he do?

WHY did he do it?

WORDS AND MEANINGS

bumbling—clumsy and mixed up

gumshoe—detective

masquerade—pretend to be someone

bent on—determined to do something

domination—having power over something

QUESTIONS

1. **WHO** is the TV show about?
   __ a. a detective and a mad scientist
   __ b. a caveman and a dinosaur
   __ c. a rocket and a rhino

2. **WHAT** did the bumbling gumshoe do?
   __ a. fought a caveman
   __ b. pretended to be a caveman
   __ c. became a mad scientist

3. **WHY** did he do it?
   __ a. to fight a mammoth
   __ b. to fly in a rocket
   __ c. to trap a mad scientist

4. Edna is going to a masquerade party. Which is the best way to dress?
   __ a. as the Queen of England
   __ b. as usual
   __ c. in her best clothes

5. Someone who is "bent on world domination" wants to be—
   __ a. a doctor
   __ b. a dictator
   __ c. a gumshoe

16. WHEN

The word **WHEN** asks a question about time. The answer may be —

- Time on a **clock**: seconds, minutes, hours
- Time on a **calendar**: days, dates, years
- Time **before**, **after**, or even **at the same time as** something else

Read the two sentences below. Think about what kind of answer you get if you ask the question **WHEN**.

1. The YMCA will give free heart check-ups on Monday, January 12

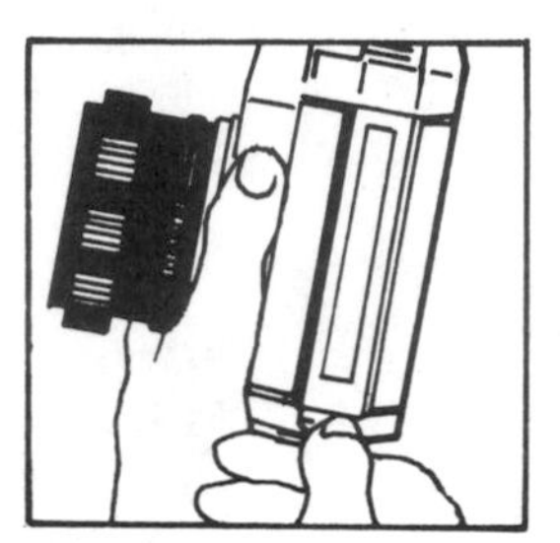

2. Rewind the film before opening your camera.

QUESTIONS

1. In Sentence 1, the answer to the question **WHEN** is the heart check-up is —

   ___ a. a time on a clock

   ___ b. a time on a calendar

   ___ c. a time before something

2. In Sentence 2, the answer to the question **WHEN** do you rewind the film is —

   ___ a. a time on a clock

   ___ b. a time on a calendar

   ___ c. a time before something

3. Read this sentence:

   He gets angry every time he has to wait.

   Here, **WHEN** is —

   ___ a. before

   ___ b. after

   ___ c. at the same time

4. Read this sentence:

   Go to Window 7 after you fill out Form 36A.

   Which do you do first?

   ___ a. go to Window 7

   ___ b. fill out Form 36A

5. Read this sentence:

   The price of orange juice has jumped since the freeze in Florida.

   This means that orange juice cost more —

   ___ a. before the freeze

   ___ b. after the freeze

   ___ c. at the same time as the freeze

6. Read this sentence:

   Press down on the gas pedal as you lift up on the clutch.

   This means —

   ___ a. lift up on the clutch first

   ___ b. press down on the gas pedal first

   ___ c. do both at the same time

17. PAST, PRESENT, AND FUTURE

Another meaning of **WHEN** is, "Is this happening in the past, present or future?"

Read the paragraph below. It is from a newspaper report. As you read, ask yourself **WHEN**. Look for two kinds of information with these questions:

- whether the time is past, present, or future
- what happened before or after

from a NEWSPAPER STORY

The Mojave Bridge fell last night after a ship lost control in the storm and crashed into one of the supports. Twenty people were rescued, but others may have been killed. Divers will begin to search the wreckage after the storm dies down.

QUESTIONS

1. "A ship lost control..."
   When does this part of the story take place?
   __ a. in the past
   __ b. in the present (now)
   __ c. in the future

2. "Divers will begin to search the wreckage..."
   When does this part of the story take place?
   __ a. in the past
   __ b. in the present (now)
   __ c. in the future

3. At the time the story was written, the storm —
   __ a. was over
   __ b. was still going on
   __ c. was coming

4. The search by the divers is in—
   __ a. past time
   __ b. present time
   __ c. future time

18. WHERE AND HOW

Read the directions below. They contain information that answers the questions **WHERE** and **HOW**.

from a SAFETY CARD ON AN AIRPLANE

To inflate the life jacket, pull down sharply on the two tabs at the sides of the jacket.

QUESTIONS

1. **WHERE** are the tabs that inflate the life jacket?
   __ a. inside the jacket
   __ b. in a pocket
   __ c. at the sides

2. **HOW** do you inflate it?
   __ a. push down slowly on the tabs
   __ b. hold the tabs and give a quick, hard, downward pull
   __ c. rip out the tabs and throw them away

3. Which sentence below tells **HOW** something must be done?
   __ a. You must work carefully to do this job.
   __ b. You must do it tomorrow.
   __ c. Pick up the package at Rubin's Drug Store.

4. Which sentence below tells **WHERE** something is done?
   __ a. Rent an electric sander at half price.
   __ b. Rent an electric sander if your floors need fixing up.
   __ c. Rent an electric sander at Keith and Nelson's.

5. Underline the words in the sentence below that tell **WHERE** something must be done.
   Place a check mark in the boxes.

6. Underline the words in the sentence below that tell **HOW** something must be done.
   Write in capital letters only.

19. WHICH ONE

Read the paragraphs below. They are from a booklet on building. They help you choose the right tools and materials for fastening wood together.

When you want to notice the difference between one or more choices, ask yourself the questions **WHICH ONE** or **WHICH ONES**.

from a BOOKLET ON BUILDING THINGS OF WOOD

NAILS come in two main shapes.

Box nails have large heads. Use them for rough work when appearance doesn't matter.

Finishing nails have small heads. You can drive them below the surface and fill in the hole and leave a smooth surface.

SCREWS are best when extra strength is important.

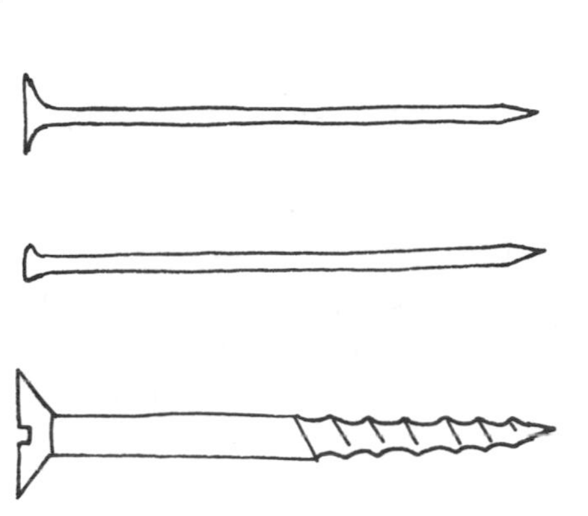

QUESTIONS

1. **WHICH ONE** is best when you want a completely smooth surface, but you don't need a lot of strength?

   __ a. box nail

   __ b. finishing nail

   __ c. screw

2. **WHICH ONE** is best when extra strength is not needed and neither is a neat appearance?

   __ a. box nail

   __ b. finishing nail

   __ c. screw

3. **WHICH ONE** is best for attaching hinges to a door? Hinges have to hold a lot of weight.

   __ a. box nail

   __ b. finishing nail

   __ c. screw

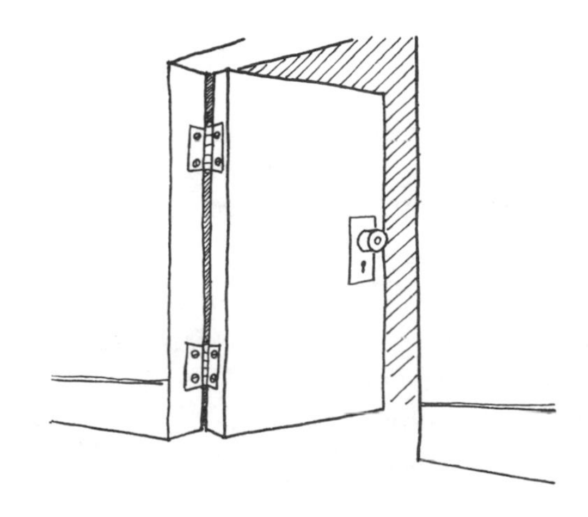

20. WHO, WHAT, WHY, WHEN, WHERE, HOW, & WHICH ONE

Read the paragraph below. It is from a booklet on storing foods.
Ask yourself the seven questions as you read.

from a BOOKLET ON STORING FOODS

WHERE IS YOUR ORANGE JUICE AFTER BREAKFAST?

You should never leave orange juice sitting around in an open container. Always cover the container and keep it in the refrigerator. Both heat and air destroy vitamin C in orange juice.

QUESTIONS

1. **WHO** should follow this advice?
   __ a. everybody
   __ b. only one person

2. **WHAT** does the paragraph say you should do? (Check 2 answers.)
   __ a. cover orange juice
   __ b. drink a lot of orange juice
   __ c. keep orange juice in the refrigerator

3. **WHY** should you do this? (Check 2 answers. Be sure they come from the paragraph.)
   __ a. flies cannot get in
   __ b. air destroys vitamin C
   __ c. heat destroys vitamin C

4. **WHEN** should you do this?
   __ a. anytime you are not using it
   __ b. only when it is hot

5. **WHERE** should you keep orange juice?
   __ a. does not say in paragraph
   __ b. in the refrigerator
   __ c. on the table

6. **HOW** should you store it?
   __ a. in a closed container
   __ b. in an open container

7. **WHICH ONE** of these containers is best for storing orange juice?
   __ a. closed jar
   __ b. open pitcher

from a WORKING DIVER'S MANUAL

Questions 8-14

Read the paragraph from a diving manual. Then answer questions 8-14 about it.

Whenever he goes on the job, the working diver knows that after he hits the water, he might as well be blind. His work will be done in nearly total blackness. Just about the only bits of information he can trust are the ones he gets through his fingertips.

8. **WHO** is this paragraph about?
   __ a. a diver
   __ b. a person on vacation
   __ c. everyone who reads it

9. **WHAT** happens to him?
   __ a. he cannot feel
   __ b. he cannot see
   __ c. he finds treasure

10. **WHY** does it happen?
    __ a. it is dark
    __ b. his eyes are covered
    __ c. he keeps his eyes closed

11. **WHEN** does it happen?
    __ a. when he falls
    __ b. when he gets sick
    __ c. whenever he dives

12. **WHERE** does it happen?
    a. in a boat
    __ b. in his home
    __ c. under the water

13. **HOW** does he know what he is doing?
    __ a. by feeling with his fingers
    __ b. by listening
    __ c. by seeing

14. **WHICH** sense is most useful to the diver?
    __ a. hearing
    __ b. seeing
    __ c. touch

UNIT 4 REVIEW

For questions 1-7, read the paragraph below. It is from a newspaper article. Ask yourself questions as you read, using the seven question words.

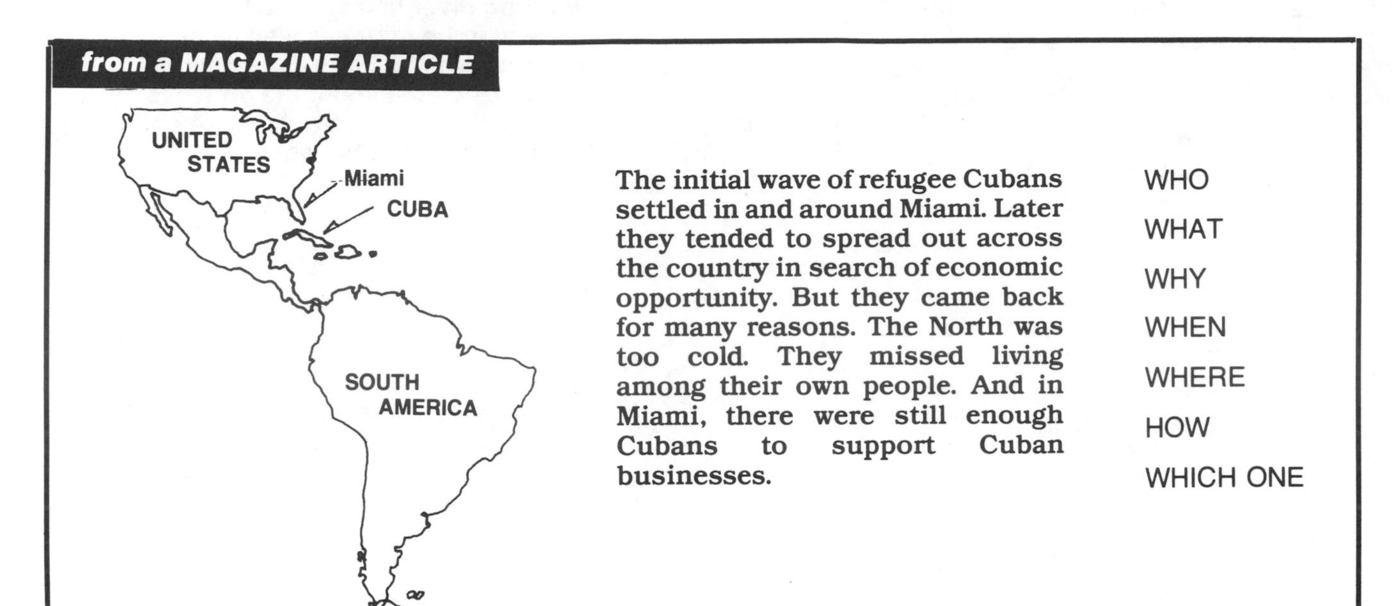

from a MAGAZINE ARTICLE

The initial wave of refugee Cubans settled in and around Miami. Later they tended to spread out across the country in search of economic opportunity. But they came back for many reasons. The North was too cold. They missed living among their own people. And in Miami, there were still enough Cubans to support Cuban businesses.

WHO
WHAT
WHY
WHEN
WHERE
HOW
WHICH ONE

WORDS AND MEANINGS

initial wave — first large group

economic opportunity — the chance to get a job and make money

refugees — people who leave their homes and their country because of danger, hunger, or politics

QUESTIONS

1. **WHO** is this paragraph talking about?
   __ a. all refugees
   __ b. Cubans who have left Cuba
   __ c. Cubans who live in Cuba

2. **WHAT** did they do?
   __ a. lost everything they ever owned
   __ b. never left Miami
   __ c. went all over the United States and came back to Miami

3. **WHY** did they do it? (Check 3 answers.)
   __ a. good for business
   __ b. good to be around other Cubans
   __ c. good weather
   __ d. laws forced them to

4. **WHEN** did they come back to Miami?
   __ a. after spreading out all over the country
   __ b. never
   __ c. they will come back soon

5. **WHERE** did they go after spreading across the country?
   __ a. back to Cuba
   __ b. back to Miami
   __ c. to South America

6. **HOW** did they do it?
   __ a. by boat
   __ b. by plane
   __ c. doesn't say in paragraph

7. **WHICH ONE** of the following places do Cubans seem to prefer?
   __ a. Miami
   __ b. New York
   __ c. doesn't say in paragraph

8. When did this paragraph about Cubans take place?
   __ a. past
   __ b. present
   __ c. future

9. What did the directions for this review suggest that you do when you read for facts?
   __ a. ask yourself questions
   __ b. memorize the facts
   __ c. take notes

10. What are the 7 Questions? Complete the list below:
   __ 1. Who
   __ 2. What
   __ 3. Why
   __ 4. W__________
   __ 5. W__________
   __ 6. H__________
   __ 7. W________ O________

from a LETTER FROM THE CITY GOVERNMENT

Read the paragraph below. It is part of a letter from the Department of Sanitation. This is the city department that has the job of keeping the city clean.

To help clean up the city, 1500 civic groups, tenants organizations, and block associations have been sent photographs of garbage problems that appear throughout the city. When you receive them, please circle the problems seen in your area, give the location, and return the photos and forms.

WORDS AND MEANINGS

block associations — groups of people who want to improve life on their block

tenant organizations—groups of people living in apartments who want to improve the life where they live

department — part of a city, state, or country government that does a particular job

civic groups — groups of people who want to improve life in their cities

11. The action in Sentence 1, above, takes place in the —
   __ a. past
   __ b. present
   __ c. future

12. The action in Sentence 2, above, takes place in the —
   __ a. past
   __ b. present
   __ c. future

Unit 5
PRACTICE LESSONS

The rest of this book contains lessons that will give you practice in all the skills you have developed in the first part of this book.

Each lesson is based on a single piece of Life Skills Reading material—a letter, a set of instructions, a section of a lease, a page from a government booklet, a newspaper story or editorial, and so on. Some of the reading pieces are fairly easy, others are more difficult. They are all examples of the kinds of reading material you will be dealing with for the rest of your life. When you have finished the lessons, you will have a good grasp of an important part of your life's reading. And you will have learned the basics of how to understand these kinds of reading and how to use them in your own daily life.

21. LETTER FROM A DAY CARE CENTER

Mr. Kostamo has a six-year-old daughter. After the daughter finishes school in the afternoon, she goes to a day care center. The day care center takes care of her until her father picks her up after work.

The County Government will pay for most of the day care charges for Mr. Kostamo's daughter because Mr. Kostamo has such a low income. Mr. Kostamo just got the letter below.

PENNSYLVANIA
SCOTT COUNTY
3000 Dexter Road
Scott, PA 17222
Office for Children—Extended Day Care

Date: September 23, 1986

Dear Mr. Kostamo,

The registration material checked below has not been received:

- [ ] Signed Application Form
- [ ] Medical Emergency Authorization
- [x] Proof of Income (i.e., paycheck stub from most recent pay period, copy of W-2 form, or statement from employer). Full fees will be charged without this verification.

Please complete this information and send to the EDC office by October 15. We cannot continue to hold a place for your child(ren) after that date.

Sincerely,

Merrily Jones

Merrily Jones
Finance Specialist

WORDS AND MEANINGS

Extended Day Care (EDC) — care for children before or after school

Medical Emergency Authorization — permission to take a child to a doctor in an emergency

i.e. — short for "that is"

W-2 form — form which an employer sends once each year to each employee stating the amount the employee earned in that year

verification — proof

QUESTIONS

1. What is the Main Idea of the letter on the last page?
   __ a. paycheck stubs must be from recent period
   __ b. send Proof of Income to EDC by October 15
   __ c. your child will not be accepted

2. Mr. Kostamo cannot find his W-2 form or paycheck stub. What should he do?
   __ a. ask his boss to write a letter with the information
   __ b. write a letter himself giving the information
   __ c. nothing, they won't throw out a 6-year-old child

3. What does "verification" mean?
   __ a. a lot of something
   __ b. financial information
   __ c. showing something is true

4. When you read the letters i.e., what do you expect to see next?
   __ a. an example of what was written before
   __ b. a new idea

5. What will be the effect if Mr. Kostamo cannot prove his low income?
   __ a. EDC will get in touch with his employer
   __ b. he will have to pay the complete costs of day care
   __ c. he will have to pay a fine

22. AUTO INSURANCE ID CARD

INSURANCE IDENTIFICATION CARD

Both the front and the back of a New York State Auto Insurance Identification Card are shown below.

FRONT OF CARD

FS-20 (9/76)
Company Code

NEW YORK STATE INSURANCE
IDENTIFICATION CARD

9123

Amos
LIFE & CASUALTY

999 THE AMOS INSURANCE CO.

Office issuing this card: JAMESWAY BROKERAGE INC.
17 Main St.
Central City, NY 12311

An authorized NEW YORK insurer has issued an Owner's Policy of Liability Insurance complying with Article 6 (Motor Vehicle Financial Security Act) of the NEW YORK Vehicle and Traffic Law to:

LISA KIM
4230 Hazel Circle
Central City, NY 12312

Effective Date	Expiration Date	Policy Number
10-23-85	10-23-86	06 BV 6284446 ABC

Applicable with respect to the following Motor Vehicle:

Year	Make	Vehicle Identification Number	Authorized Representative
82	OPEL	572606949	William O. Baily

(SEE IMPORTANT MESSAGE ON REVERSE SIDE)

BACK OF CARD

THIS CARD MUST BE CARRIED IN THE INSURED VEHICLE
FOR PRODUCTION UPON DEMAND

WARNING: Any person who issues or produces this card to show that there is in force a policy of insurance as indicated herein,that is in fact not in effect, is liable to a heavy fine and/or imprisonment and his license and/or registration may be suspended or revoked.

Report All Auto Accidents Immediately.

- DURING BUSINESS HOURS, call (collect) the nearest Amos Insurance Claim Office.
- AFTER BUSINESS HOURS, or if unable to contact an Amos Claims Office, call, toll free (800) 222-5635.
- IN CONNECTICUT, call (collect) 225-4633.

WORDS AND MEANINGS

insurance identification card—proof that your car is insured. Tells what insurance company you have and what the policy number is.

issuing—sending out

authorized New York insurer—insurance company which is allowed ("authorized") to do business in New York

insurer—insurance company

owner's policy—insurance policy

liability insurance—insurance that pays for damages you cause someone else

complying—agreeing with. Does what it is supposed to.

Article 6—part of a law. In this case, part of the law called the "Motor Vehicle Financial Security Act."

vehicle—car or truck

reverse side—on the back

for production upon demand—ready to show to someone who asks to see it. The person who has the right to ask to see it might be a police officer, or someone from another car who is in an accident with your car.

in force—still in effect, still active

liable (to fine and/or imprisonment)—in danger of, apt to get a fine and/or be sent to jail.

license—in this case, a driver's license. Allows you to drive a car

registration—in this case, a car registration. A license for your car.

suspended—taken away for a period of time

revoked—taken away forever

(call) collect—the insurance company will pay the phone charges

toll free—the company has a special telephone number, and it won't cost anything to call this number

QUESTIONS

1. Read the front of the card.
   What is the Main Idea of the section that begins: "An authorized NEW YORK insurer has..."?
   __ a. shows that Lisa Kim has insurance for her car
   __ b. shows what kind of insurance company Lisa Kim went to
   __ c. shows where the insurance company has its offices

2. Who sent out the card to Lisa Kim?
   __ a. Amos Insurance Co.
   __ b. Jamesway Brokerage

3. Read the back of the card.
   What is the Main Idea of the section that says: "WARNING"?
   __ a. be careful never to lose this card
   __ b. don't use a phony card
   __ c. this card will protect you in case of accident

4. Match—

__ front of card	A. gives details about Lisa Kim's insurance
__ back of card	B. tells Lisa how to use the card

5. Look at the back of the card again.
   At the bottom it tells Lisa to report all accidents immediately. How does it tell her to make such a report?
   __ a. by letter
   __ b. by phone
   __ c. in person

6. Look at the top of the card, on the back.
   Where is Lisa supposed to keep the card?
   __ a. at the insurance office
   __ b. in a safe place at home
   __ c. with her in the car

27. CONSUMER INFORMATION

Below is part of a list of consumer shopping hints.

CONSUMER SHOPPING HINTS

1. In the supermarket, compare prices. To do this look for the Unit Prices on the shelf labels.
2. Look for the date stamped on perishable food.
3. Read the labels on all packaged foods. The ingredient listed first is the thing there is the most of in the container.
4. Get a written estimate before having repair work done.
5. Be sure you get an itemized bill before you pay for any repairs.
6. Shop around and compare prices and quality before making any major purchase.

WORDS AND MEANINGS

consumer — person who buys things or services (such as repairs or haircuts)

Unit Price — the price for each "unit" of something. Can be price per pound, or price per ounce, not per serving, for example. Helps compare prices even if sizes are different.

perishible—food that won't last

ingredients — what a product contains or is made of

itemized bill — breaking down the total bill into separate amounts for each new part used and for the labor needed

major purchase — big and expensive item, such as a car or a TV or a stove or a refrigerator

estimate — the amount the repair person thinks it will cost to do the job

QUESTIONS

1. You want to know which brand of ketchup costs the least per pound. What should you look at?
   __ a. amount you pay
   __ b. unit price

UNIT PRICE	YOU PAY
60.6¢ PER POUND	53¢
Kitchen Pride Ketchup	

UNIT PRICE	YOU PAY
58.0¢ PER POUND	72¢
Saucy Ketchup	

2. Below is part of a label from a package of cherry gelatin desert.

   INGREDIENTS: Sugar, gelatin, adipic acid, disodium phosphate, fumaric acid, artificial color, artificial flavor.

   What is there the most of?
   __ a. cherries
   __ b. gelatin
   __ c. sugar

3. How can you tell which milk is freshest?
   __ a. by asking the store to pour you some samples
   __ b. by looking at the date stamped on the cartons
   __ c. by looking for the cartons at the back

4. What is an estimate?
   __ a. a bill for a repair job
   __ b. the part of the bill that pays for labor
   __ c. what a repair person thinks a job will cost

5. You have just gone to pick up your TV set after some repairs. The repair person gives you the bill below.

   UNCLE SAM'S TV REPAIRS
   BILL

   TOTAL DUE........$200

   You should ask for an ____________ bill.

24. COOKING DIRECTIONS

Below is a set of directions for cooking macaroni.

If you do not follow the directions, the macaroni may be too mushy, or too hard, or it may stick together in clumps.

cooking directions

- **Add 1 tablespoon salt to 3 quarts of rapidly boiling water. Gradually add contents of this package so that water does not stop boiling.**
- **Boil, uncovered, 9 to 12 minutes or until desired tenderness; stir occasionally. DO NOT OVERCOOK. Boil only 6 to 7 minutes when using in a casserole or other recipe where it will receive further cooking.**
- **Drain thoroughly in a colander. Then serve as quickly as possible, or continue with your recipe. IF USING IN A COLD SALAD, rinse with cold water and drain again.**

WORDS AND MEANINGS

enriched — some vitamins or minerals needed for health have been added

colander — a type of strainer for draining water off food

casserole — a mixture of ingredients baked in the oven (such as baked noodles and tuna fish)

QUESTIONS

1. How hot or cold should the water be when you add the macaroni?
   __ a. cold, fresh from the faucet
   __ b. hot, but not quite boiling
   c. boiling fast with lots of bubbles

2. When should the salt be added?
   __ a. before adding the macaroni
   __ b. after boiling the macaroni
   __ c. after draining the macaroni

3. Should the pan be covered while cooking the macaroni?
   __ yes __ no

4. Which is an example of a casserole?
   __ a. chicken and noodle soup
   __ b. fried chicken
   __ c. small pieces of chicken baked in a sauce with noodles

5. Below are two ways to serve macaroni. Match (fill in the blanks with the right letters).

TIME	WAY TO SERVE
__ 9 to 12 minutes	a. You plan to mix it with a sauce and bake it in the oven
__ 6 to 7 minutes	b. You plan to pour a tomato sauce over it and put it on the table

6. You plan to use the macaroni in a cold salad with tuna fish. What should you do?
   __ a. let it sit—do not drain
   __ b. pour cold water over the macaroni and drain it again

7. Which looks like the piece of kitchen equipment that you should use in the last step?

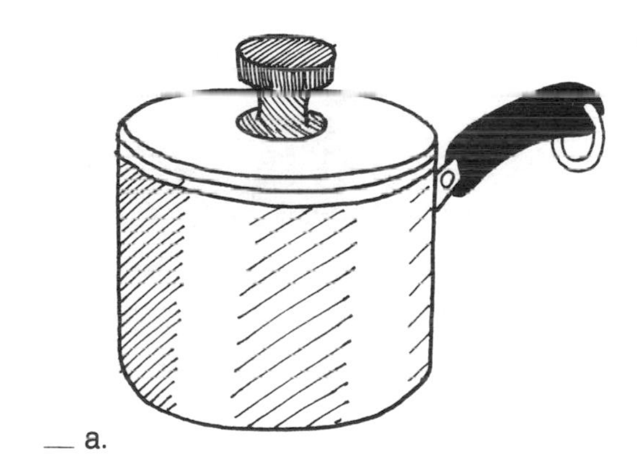

__ a.

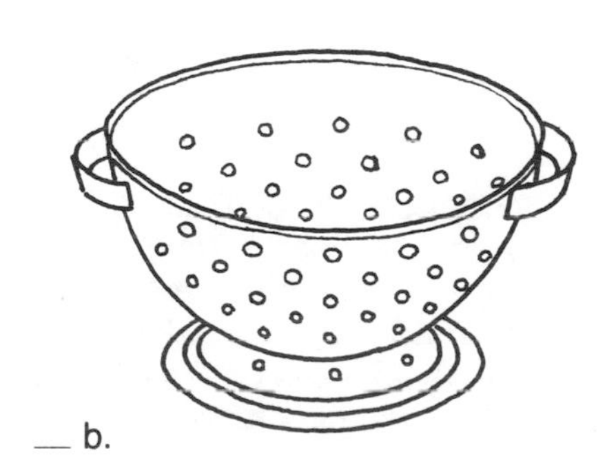

__ b.

25. RECIPE

A recipe is a set of directions that tell you how to cook something.

Recipes are printed in cookbooks, magazines, newspapers, even on the sides of packages.

Read the recipe for baked macaroni and cheese, below.

baked macaroni and cheese

2 tablespoons butter or margarine
2 tablespoons flour
1 teaspoon salt
1 teaspoon dry mustard
2½ cups milk
2 cups (8 ounces) shredded cheese (use mild or sharp process or Cheddar as you prefer)
8 ounces (2 cups) Mueller's elbow macaroni
¼ cup buttered bread crumbs
Paprika

In saucepan, melt butter. Remove from heat; blend in flour, salt, and mustard. Add milk; heat, stirring constantly, until sauce thickens a little and is smooth. Add 1½ cups cheese; heat until melted, stirring occasionally. Meanwhile, cook macaroni as directed; drain. Combine with sauce in a 2-quart casserole; top with remaining cheese, bread crumbs, and paprika. Bake at 375° F. about 20 to 25 minutes or until nicely browned and bubbly. Makes 4 to 6 servings.

WORDS AND MEANINGS

tablespoon—a special large measuring spoon. Don't use the kind you eat with.

teaspoon—a small measuring spoon. Three of them make a tablespoon. Don't use the kind you eat with.

cup—a special glass or metal cup used to measure liquid in cooking. Don't use an ordinary drinking cup.

shredded — cut up into little thin slices

sharp cheese — cheese with a strong taste

Cheddar cheese — a kind of cheese that is often used in cooking (or in toasted cheese sandwiches). Can be mild or sharp.

elbow macaroni — short, stubby macaroni that looks like this:

paprika — a mild red seasoning. It comes in a powder.

saucepan — a kind of pan you use to boil water

blend — mix in

casserole (dish)—a kind of dish you use to bake casseroles (see last lesson). A casserole dish won't break from the heat when you bake something.

QUESTIONS

1. CIRCLE the spoon below to be used to measure out the dry mustard.

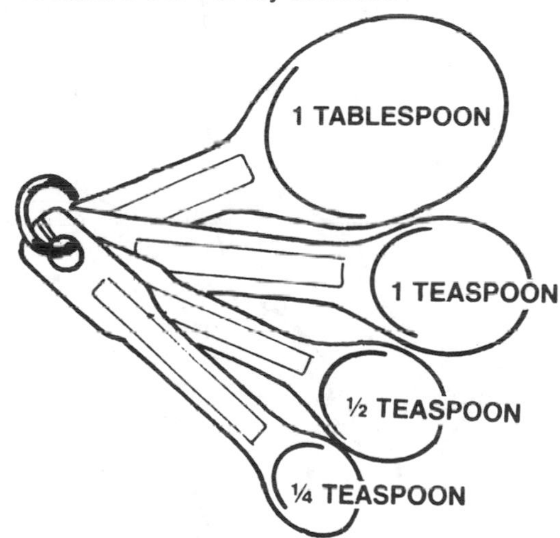

TEASPOON FOR EATING

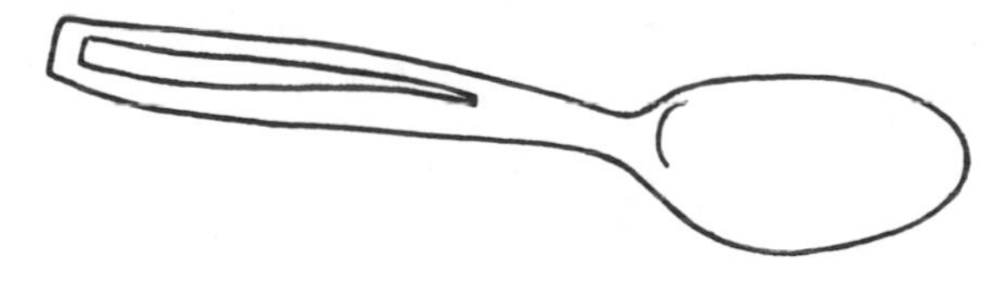

2. After you add the cheese, how do you decide the sauce is finished?

__ a. by timing it

__ b. by watching it

3. Which picture below shows the right amount of shredded cheese to melt into the sauce?

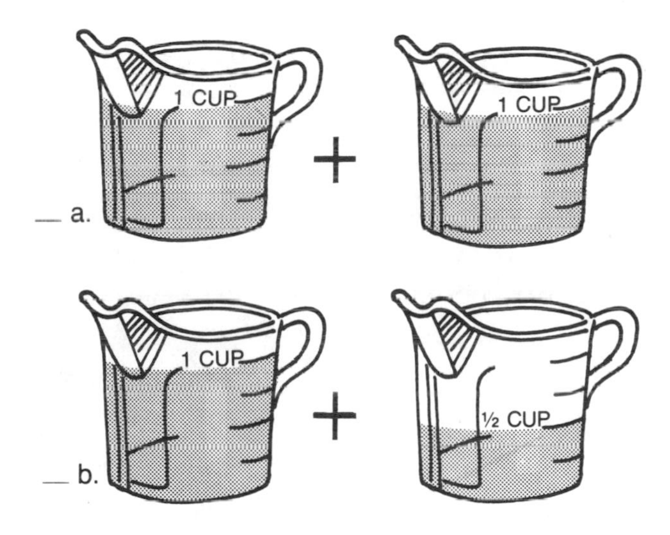

4. What kind of dish should you bake the macaroni and cheese in?

__ a. a sauce pan

__ b. any glass dish

__ c. a glass dish made especially to take heat

5. Sam fixed this recipe for himself and his wife. Which is most likely?

_ a. he will have some left over

_ b. he will not have enough

26. REPAIR DIRECTIONS

The directions below are from a booklet on home repairs.

HOW TO REPAIR A LEAKY FAUCET

1. First turn off the water at the shut-off valve nearest the faucet you are going to repair. (Fig. 1)
2. Then turn on the faucet until the water stops flowing.
3. Loosen the packing nut with wrench. (Fig. 2)
4. Use the handle to pull out the unit. (Fig. 3)
5. Remove screw holding old washer at the bottom of the valve unit. (Fig. 4)
6. Choose a new washer the same size as the old one. (Fig. 5)
7. Put in the new washer and replace the screw. (Fig. 6)
8. Put valve unit back in faucet. Turn handle to proper position.
9. Tighten the packing nut. (Fig. 7)
10. Turn on the water at the shut-off valve.

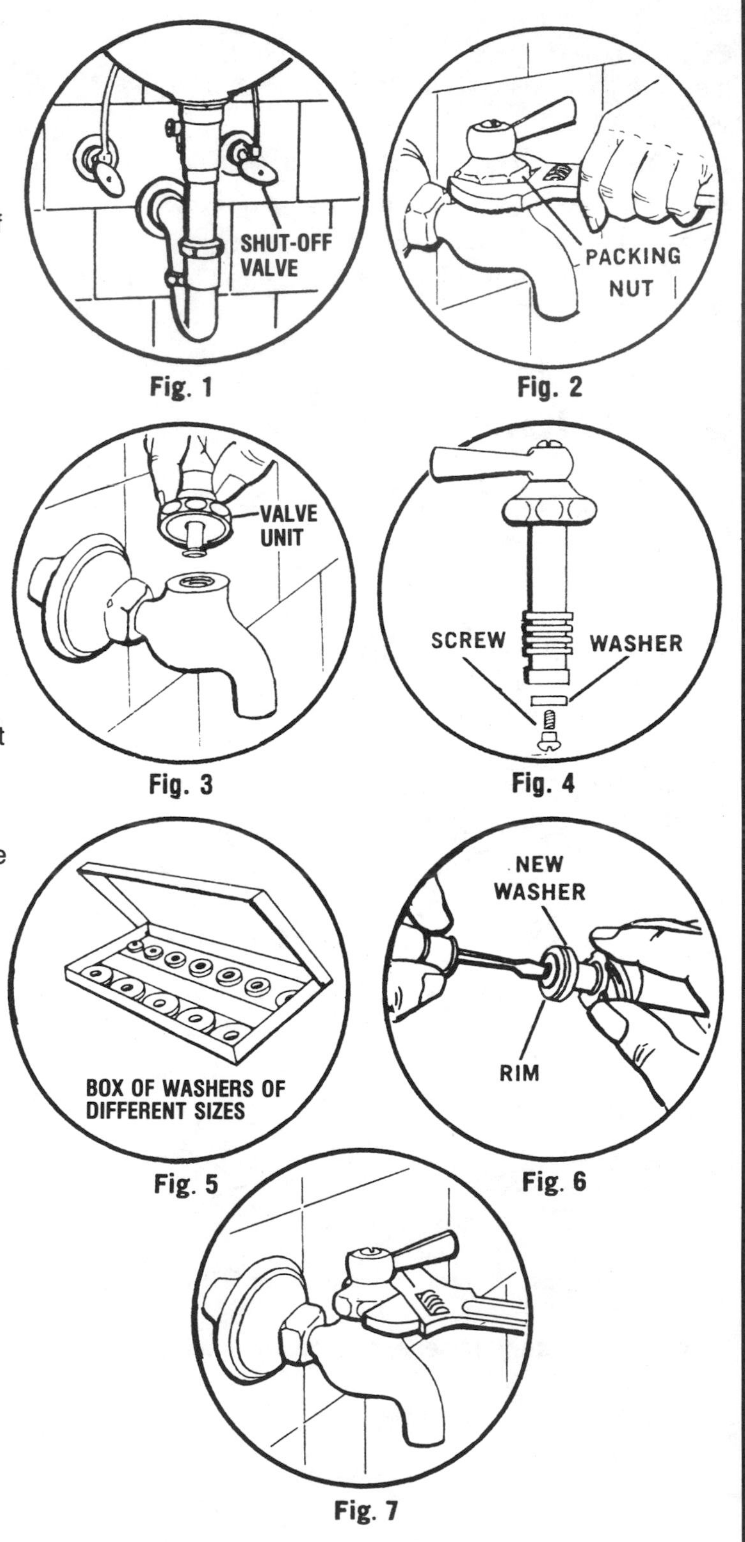

WORDS AND MEANINGS

valve — in plumbing, a part you turn on or off to let water in or keep it out. There are shut-off valves below a sink. You can turn them off to work on the faucets.

packing nut — seals the unit and keeps it tight. See picture.

wrench — this tool:

washer — flat ring used to help make tight connections. Washers in faucets are rubber or plastic. The ones you use to keep nuts and bolts tight are often made of metal.

QUESTIONS

1. What is the first step in fixing a leaky faucet?
   __ a. run water
   __ b. turn off shut-off valve

2. What is the next step?
   __ a. take the faucet out
   __ b. turn the water on until it stops flowing

3. Where can you look to see what a shut-off valve might look like?
   __ Figure 1
   __ Figure 2
   __ Figure 3

4. Which part of this picture shows the packing nut?
   __ A __ B __ C

5. Which picture shows how to pull out the valve unit?
   __ Figure 1
   __ Figure 2
   __ Figure 3

6. Which picture shows how to take off the old washer?
   __ Figure 4
   __ Figure 5
   __ Figure 6

7. Are all washers the same size?
   __ yes __ no

8. What tool do you need in Figure 6?
   __ a. screwdriver
   __ b. wrench

9. What is the last step?
   __ a. putting the valve unit in place
   __ b. turning on the shut-off valve

27. JOB VACANCY LIST

Below is a list of job openings in the Foxfield Hospital. Many jobs in hospitals have to be done days, nights, and weekends. If there are job openings at different times of day, each is listed on a separate line below.

The Foxfield Hospital
8752 W. Hurley Road
Foxfield, Georgia 30555

Tel: 423-4567

JOB VACANCY LIST 8/4/86 EXPIRES 8/8/86

MEDICAL RECORDS

Clerk - Varied duties including the pulling and assembling of charts from master files. Must be able to sort and file. Previous clerical experience desirable.

Mon-Thurs 5:00 pm - 10:00 pm and
Fri 4:00 pm - 8:00 pm (24) P/T

Mon-Fri Mid-8:30 am (40) F/T

Mon-Fri 8:00 am - 4:30 pm (40) F/T

Page Operator - Operate the physician's paging system and assist in the assembling of medical records of newly discharged patients.

Sat Noon - 8:30 (8) P/T

Mon-Fri Noon - 8:30 pm (40) F/T

Adminstrative Secretary - Diversified secretarial duties assisting the Director of Medical Records. Take dictation, type letters, notices, etc., sort and distribute mail, answer phone and screen calls, maintain files and perform various duties as necessary. Previous secretarial and public contact experience, 60 WPM typing and 80 WPM shorthand required.

Mon-Fri 8:00 am - 4:30 pm (40) F/T

WORDS AND MEANINGS

job vacancy—a job that on one is doing,and needs someone to do it. A job vacancy list is like a "help wanted" list.

master files — main files of patient records

previous — earlier

(40) F/T — 40 hours of work each week, Full Time (F/T)

(24) P/T — 24 hours of work each week, Part Time (P/T)

physician's paging system — public address system to call doctors anywhere in a hospital

taking dictation — writing down what someone says, using shorthand for speed

diversified — many different kinds

etc. — abbreviation for et cetera. It means "and other things." It is used when a list is getting too long

public contact — meeting people, dealing with the public

WPM — words per minute

QUESTIONS

1. Which job is best for someone who wants a full-time job working nights?
   __ a. clerk
   __ b. page operator
   __ c. administrative secretary

2. Andrea got the Saturday job as a page operator. How many hours a week will she work?
   __ 8 __ 24 __ 40

3. Which picture at the right do you think shows a job with more public contact?
   __ Picture A __ Picture B

4. Look for the abbreviation etc. in the administrative secretary listing. What does it mean?
   __ a. all the things to be typed in addition to letters and notices
   __ b. employee time control
   __ c. employee typing speed

5. How fast should the administrative secretary be able to take dictation?
   __ a. 30 words each second
   __ b. 50 words each minute
   __ c. 80 words each minute

6. What does the page operator do?
   __ a. calls doctors over a public address system
   __ b. calls patients over the telephone
   __ c. pulls charts from master files

Picture A

Picture B

28. NEWSPAPER EDITORIAL

Below is an editorial from the South Shore Times newspaper.

An editorial is not a news report. It is a statement of the writer's opinion. It tells what the newspaper thinks about something.

When you read an editorial, look for the facts it states. Look for the writer's opinion. And look to see if the opinion is backed up by the facts.

Shifting Principals

Red Sambur has been the much-loved principal of East Bay Elementary School for 14 years. Now, if School Superintendent Jane Hankins has her way, Red is going to be reassigned all the way across the district. According to Superintendent Hankins' plan, Red will replace Mary Orlando next September as principal of Swamp Hollow Elementary School. The proposed move, announced yesterday at a School Board meeting, is part of a wholesale shift in administrators. Where is Mary Orlando expected to go? The plan is for her to take over Red Sambur's post at East Bay.

In announcing the new assignments, Superintendent Hankins said the shift was needed to "keep the schools from getting too set in their ways."

The real truth is that Superintendent Hankins wants to have more control over the district. The plan is politics at its worst, a power grab by Superintendent Hankins.

Our individual schools have always prided themselves on being different. Each school meets the needs of its neighborhood community. Principals, teachers, and parents have learned to work well together.

The South Shore Times urges its readers to oppose this plan. We think it is a bad plan. We think it is a plan that should be stopped by the people of this community.

WORDS AND MEANINGS

superintendent (of schools)—head of a school system

reassigned—moved to a new job location

proposed—suggested, planned

shift—moving around. A "wholesale shift" is moving around a lot of people, all at once.

administrators—people who run things

post—job, position

power grab—a move someone makes to get a lot of power

prided themselves—been proud of

QUESTIONS

1. What does Superintendent Hankins want to do?
   __ a. shift administrators from one school to another
   __ b. make sure administrators stay in their old jobs
   __ c. give administrators the choice

2. According to the plan, next September Red Sambur will be principal of—
   __ a. East Day Elementary School
   __ b. South Shore Elementary School
   __ c. Swamp Hollow Elementary School

3. What does the South Shore Times think of the plan?
   __ a. likes it
   __ b. dislikes it
   __ c. doesn't care

4. Who is Mary Orlando?
   __ a. school prinicpal
   __ b. superintendent of schools
   __ c. writer for South Shore Times

5. What is the main point of the last paragraph of the article?
   __ a. tells readers there is nothing they can do
   __ b. tells readers to make up their own minds
   __ c. tells readers to oppose the plan

29. UNEMPLOYMENT INSURANCE HANDBOOK

The table of contents of the handbook is shown at the left below. The section on Reporting to the Office is shown on the right. Read the section on the right.

Unemployment Insurance

Handbook for Claimants

INTERSTATE

☒ **Identification Card**

☒ **Information on Claims**

KEEP THIS ALL DURING YOUR CLAIM

STATE OF CALIFORNIA
EMPLOYMENT DEVELOPMENT DEPARTMENT

REPORTING TO THE OFFICE

You are given a regular day and time to report. To help us serve you promptly, report on time, but please do not come too early. Reporting on time helps prevent overcrowding in the office lobby and helps you receive better service.

If you miss your report time, contact your local office as soon as possible. You may lose benefits or waiting period credit for the weeks you are claiming if you miss a day.

When you report, we may refer you to a job. You should be dressed appropriately so we can refer you directly to an employer. Also you should not be restricted by anything that would prevent you from reporting directly to a job, such as having children with you.

If you get a job and finish that work, you may come in and reopen your claim right away. If you wait for your regular report day you may lose a week's credit.

Benefit payments may be held up sometimes by the paying state if there is any question about your eligibility. Be sure to report to the local office and complete a

(7)

WORDS AND MEANINGS

Unemployment Insurance—money the state pays you each week when you are out of work after losing a job. There are many rules that tell whether a person can or cannot get such Unemployment Insurance pay.

report—come to the Unemployment Insurance Office

claim—request for benefits

benefits—money paid to people whose claims are accepted

office—in this case, the Unemployment Insurance office

waiting period—the time after you make a claim, but before you begin to get paid your benefits

refer—send

appropriately—properly. In this paragraph, "dressing appropriately" means dressing in the proper clothes for the work you usually do.

restricted—held back

eligibility—whether or not you qualify, or are "eligible" for benefits

QUESTIONS

1. What is the Main Idea of just the first paragraph?
   __ a. don't come too early
   __ b. report on time on the right day
   __ c. overcrowding is the worst problem about Unemployment Insurance

2. Lena is supposed to come between 4:15 and 4:45. Traffic is terrible at 4:00. Should she come at 3:30?
   __ yes __ no

3. Harry forgot to go to the office on Thursday. He remembered it late Thursday night. When should he go back to the office?
   __ a. Friday morning
   __ b. next Thursday at his regular time
   __ c. he should not go back because he has lost his rights

4. Are all unemployed people who want to work eligible for Unemployment Insurance benefits?
   __ yes __ no

5. All the people described below are in the office on time. Which of them is still not following directions? (Check more than one.)
   __ a. Akira is wearing jeans and a T-shirt, just as he usually wears fixing roofs.
   __ b. Dianne is wearing jeans and a T-shirt. She is a bank teller.
   __ c. Sandy has to go to a baseball game as soon as he leaves the office.
   __ d. Tess is too broke to hire a baby sitter, so she has her 4-year-old with her.

6. Brad had a job for a few days. It just finished. What could be the effect of waiting until his regular day to come into the office?
   __ a. losing a week of credit
   __ b. losing all his benefits
   __ c. no effect—it's the right thing to do

30. CHARGE ACCOUNT AGREEMENT—Part 1

Below is part of a Charge Account Agreement with T.L. Landes Co., a large department store.

T.L. LANDES CO.

CHARGE ACCOUNT AGREEMENT

TIME PAYMENT ACCOUNT

1. **PARTIES TO AGREEMENT**—In this agreement, you and your mean everyone who signs the agreement. We, us, and our mean T.L. Landes Co., Inc.
2. **PROMISE TO PAY**—You must pay for all purchases you charge, and for all purchases of anyone you allow to use your account.
3. **BILLING STATEMENTS**—You will receive a Billing Statement once each month. It will state your NEW BALANCE and the MINIMUM PAYMENT DUE. Your NEW BALANCE is what you owed when the statement was made. It will tell PAYMENTS you made during the month and PURCHASES you bought. It will also list the FINANCE CHARGE, if any.
4. **FINANCE CHARGE**—If you pay less than the NEW BALANCE, we will add a FINANCE CHARGE to your BALANCE each month until it has been paid. If you pay the entire NEW BALANCE, there will be no FINANCE CHARGE for that month. The faster you pay the balance, the less FINANCE CHARGE you will have to pay.

YOUR SIGNATURE MEANS THAT YOU HAVE READ AND AGREE TO THE TERMS OF OUR CHARGE ACCOUNT AGREEMENT

Date 7/16/87

Applicant's signature

Colleen Ritter

Co-applicant's signature

Daisy Ritter

WORDS AND MEANINGS

charge account—lets you buy things and "charge" them (pay for them later)

time payment account—you can pay for what you buy over a period of several months

parties to an agreement—people who are making an agreement

billing statement—your monthly bill

new balance—what you owe. Total of what you bought plus finance charges plus what you still owe from before.

minimum payment due—you must pay at least this amount. You may pay more if you want to.

finance charge—interest. The charge for borrowing money.

interest—the extra amount of money you agree to pay back when you borrow or buy on credit. It's like rent for using borrowed money.

co-applicant—person who is applying with another person. Colleen and Daisy are co-applicants on the previous page.

QUESTIONS

Look back at the Charge Account Agreement on the previous page.

1. Read the paragraph next to Colleen's and Daisy's signatures (at the bottom).
   What does it mean?
   __ a. signing means you agree to all the points in the agreement and you know what they are
   __ b. you don't have to know what the agreement says, since it's just legal words

2. How often will Colleen and Daisy get a billing statement?
   __ a. every month
   __ b. every time they buy something
   __ c. every time they pay their bills

3. Here is part of Colleen's and Daisy's billing statement for this month.

PREVIOUS BALANCE	PURCHASES	PAYMENTS	FINANCE CHARGE	NEW BALANCE	MINIMUM PAYMENT
$274.31	$87.36	$274.31	$0.00	$87.36	$20.00

   What is the smallest payment they can make this month?

   $________

4. Can Colleen and Daisy pay more than the minimum?
   __ yes __ no

5. Look back at Colleen's and Daisy's billing statement in Question 3.
   How much do they have to pay to keep from owing a finance charge for this month?

   $________

6. Your new balance on a charge account is—
   __ a. what you owe
   __ b. what you paid last month
   __ c. what interest the store charges

31. CHARGE ACCOUNT AGREEMENT—Part 2

Below is more of the Charge Account Agreement from the department store.

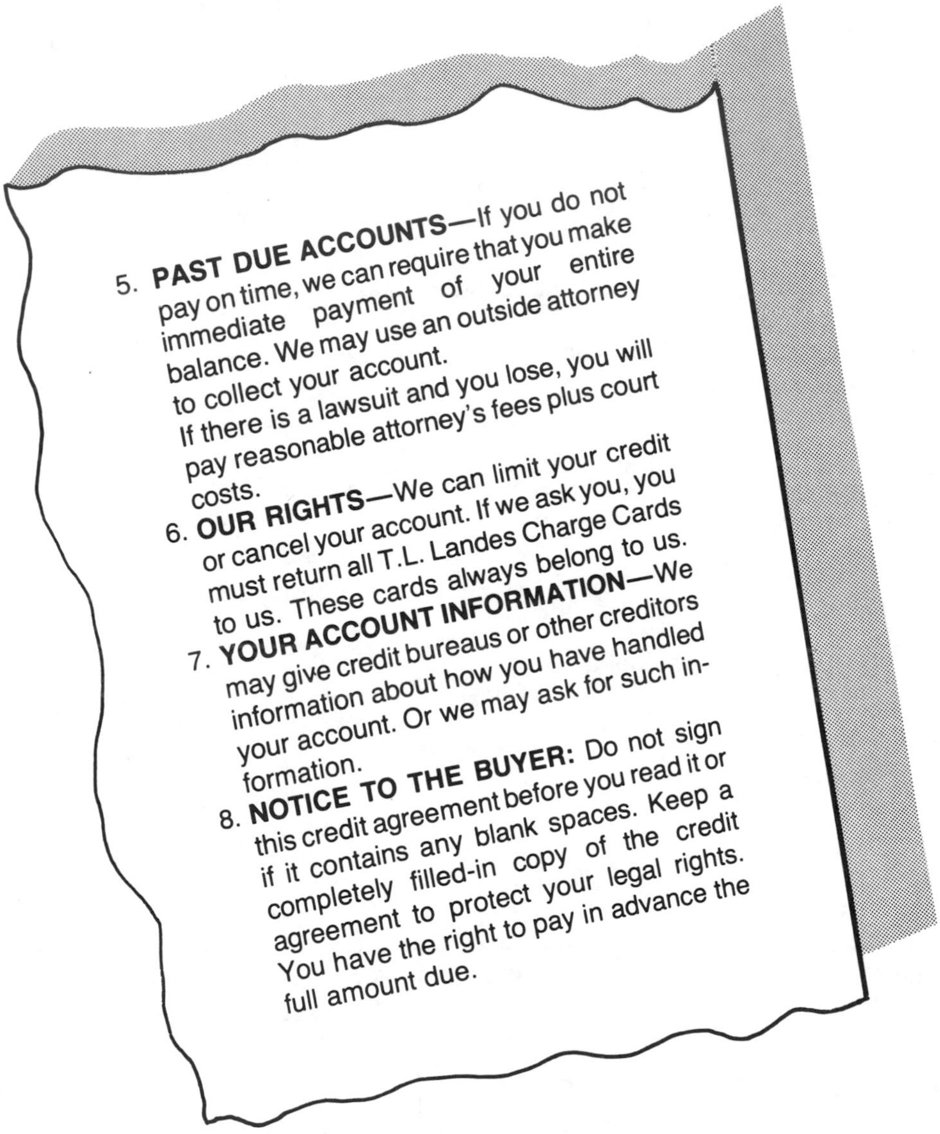

5. **PAST DUE ACCOUNTS**—If you do not pay on time, we can require that you make immediate payment of your entire balance. We may use an outside attorney to collect your account. If there is a lawsuit and you lose, you will pay reasonable attorney's fees plus court costs.
6. **OUR RIGHTS**—We can limit your credit or cancel your account. If we ask you, you must return all T.L. Landes Charge Cards to us. These cards always belong to us.
7. **YOUR ACCOUNT INFORMATION**—We may give credit bureaus or other creditors information about how you have handled your account. Or we may ask for such information.
8. **NOTICE TO THE BUYER:** Do not sign this credit agreement before you read it or if it contains any blank spaces. Keep a completely filled-in copy of the credit agreement to protect your legal rights. You have the right to pay in advance the full amount due.

WORDS AND MEANINGS

past due accounts—when you are late paying your bill

entire balance—everything you owe

attorney—lawyer

lawsuit—when you take a problem to a court of law

limit your credit—limit amount you can borrow

cancel your account—end the agreement and not let you charge what you buy

Charge Card—the card you use to charge things at the store

credit bureaus—companies which find out how likely people are to pay their bills on time

creditors—people or companies who lend money

QUESTIONS

1. This part of the agreement talks mainly about the rights of—
   __ a. the customer
   __ b. the store

2. Suppose you have a T.L. Landes Charge Account. Can T.L. Landes tell other stores how well you pay your bills?
   __ yes __ no

3. Some of T.L. Landes' customers never pay their bills on time. Does T.L. Landes have the right to end the charge account of these customers?
   __ yes __ no

4. Match—

__ pay your bills on time	A. paragraph 5
__ read it before you sign it	B. paragraph 8

5. What does paragraph 6 say about T.L. Landes Charge Cards?
   __ a. property of T.L. Landes
   __ b. you own yours, take care of it
   __ c. they come in different colors

6. Match—

__ didn't pay on time	A. Finance Charge
__ fee for borrowing	B. New Balance
__ what you owe this month	C. Past Due Account

32. BILLING ERROR NOTICE

The notice below is the type of notice that is printed on the back of credit agreements or billing statements. It tells people about their rights when they think there is a mistake on a bill.

IN CASE OF ERRORS OR INQUIRIES ABOUT YOUR BILL

The Federal Truth in Lending Act requires prompt correction of billing mistakes.

1. If you want to preserve your rights under the Act, here's what to do when you think your bill is wrong or when you need more information about an item on your bill:

    a. Do not write on the bill. On a separate sheet of paper, write the following:

        1. Your account number.
        2. A description of the error and an explanation (to the extent you can explain) why you believe it is an error.
        3. The dollar amount of the suspected error.

    b. Send your billing error notice to the address which appears on your bill after "Send Inquiries To." Mail it early enough to reach us within 60 days after the bill was mailed to you.

2. You remain obligated to pay the parts of your bill that are not in dispute, but you do not have to pay any amount in dispute during the time the creditor is resolving the dispute. During that time the creditor may not take any action to collect disputed amounts or report amounts as delinquent.

WORDS AND MEANINGS

inquiries—questions

Federal Truth in Lending Act—a law that protects people who borrow money or who buy things on credit

preserve—protect

you remain obligated—you still must

in dispute—being questioned or argued about

creditor—person or company you owe money to (not necessarily the same as where you bought the goods)

resolving—work out who is right

take action to collect disputed amounts—sue you, or send collection agencies after you

delinquent—late in payment

QUESTIONS

Part of Billing Statement Sent To Thalia Doons

DATE	PURCHASE	REFERENCE NUMBER	AMOUNT
05/23	B & W TV	8000534-BW	124.00
05/30	BOOTS	2422-030-20	80.00

1. Notice that boots are listed on the part of a billing statement above.
   Thalia says she did not buy any boots.
   What should she do?
   __ a. send in the bill with the boots crossed out
   __ b. telephone the company
   __ c. write the company about the problem

2. Where can she find where to send the letter?
   __ a. look for the name and address on the billing statement
   __ b. look for the address of the nearest branch of the store

3. What should she do about the bill for the TV while she is waiting to hear about the boots?
   __ a. pay it
   __ b. not pay it

4. What should she do about the $80 charge for the boots while she is waiting for them to decide?
   __ a. pay it
   __ b. not pay it

5. What is a creditor?
   __ a. someone who owes money
   __ b. someone money is owed to

6. If Thalia does not pay the $80 for the boots while she waits for the answer and she wrote her notice correctly, what can the company do?
   __ a. get the courts to force her to pay
   __ b. nothing until a decision has been made
   __ c. tell the other companies that she does not pay her bills on time

7. Read Thalia's letter, below. Check it against paragraph 1a of the notice. Does it have all the information that it is supposed to?
   __ yes __ no

164 West Street
Springfield, OR 87477
June 6, 1986

T.X. Landes
P.O. Box 340
New York, N.Y. 10013

To Whom it may concern:

My account number is
4213-00-21

There was an error on my last bill. I was billed $80 for a pair of boots that I did not buy. The date was 5/30/86.

33. SPORTS ARTICLE

The following article is from the Daily Sentinel.

SENTINEL SPORTS

IT'S A LONG ROAD FROM ASHEVILLE TO THE MAJOR LEAGUES

by THELMA JONES

He hit a home run on Thursday. He hit another one on Saturday in the top of the ninth inning to win the second game. The reporters wouldn't leave him alone.

It wasn't always that way. Armando Garcia rode buses from one Minor League town to another—Rockport, Illinois, Asheville, N.C., Bluefield, W. Va. Armando played for all of them. He always knew he was good enough to make the Major Leagues. But the baseball people didn't see it the same way. They would take a look at him in spring training camp. Then they'd send him down for another year in the Minor Leagues.

This year, it's different. Bobby Bushnell got hurt. Armando got his chance on June 10. Since then he's had six home runs in 11 games. He's hot. The A's are winning. Armando's been the big gun.

In good times and bad, Armando never lost his cool. Says Armando, "I just like playing baseball. Even when you're in the Minor Leagues it's wonderful to know you're getting paid to play a game you love."

WORDS AND MEANINGS

minors—teams less important than Major League teams like the New York Yankees or the Oakland A's.

QUESTIONS

1. Who wrote this newspaper article?
   ___ a. Armando Garcia
   ___ b. Bobby Bushnell
   ___ c. Thelma Jones

2. Who said, "It's wonderful to know you're getting paid to play a game you love"?
   ___ a. Armando Garcia
   ___ b. Bobby Bushnell
   ___ c. Thelma Jones

3. How did Garcia feel about the times before he got his big chance?
   ___ a. angry and bitter
   ___ b. lucky to be playing baseball
   ___ c. that he was not good enough for a Major League team

4. What was the effect of giving Garcia a chance to play for the A's?
   ___ a. A's did well
   ___ b. A's got in trouble

5. Show the time in the pictures at the right by labeling one THEN and the other NOW. You write the words in the blanks over the pictures.

6. What is the Main Idea of the article?
   ___ a. after many years in the Minor Leagues, Garcia finally got to play for the A's and is doing fine
   ___ b. Garcia was a hard hitter who quickly made his way to the big time
   ___ c. for years Garcia rode buses all over America to play baseball

____

____

34. LEASE—Part 1

Below is the top part of a lease. A lease is the agreement between the landlord and the person renting a house or apartment. Sometimes the landlord pays an agent called a realtor to take care of the property. The realtor may also sign the lease. Before signing a lease, always find out **WHAT** you are agreeing to and for **HOW LONG**.

LEASE

Notice: This lease is a legally binding contract. If you do not understand it, seek legal advice.

Lessor/Lessee/Realtor

This Lease is made as of *September 23*, **19***86*, **by and among** *Max Ryle*, **hereinafter called the Lessor, and** *Ginia Sands*, **hereinafter called the Lessee, and** *Western Management*, **hereinafter called the Realtor.**

Property Description

Lessor hereby lets to the Lessee the following property:

Location: *1444 West Lake Drive*
Thief River Falls
Polk County, Minnesota 55555

Description: *4-room apartment on second floor of a 2-family frame house*

Term and Rent

The property is let for the term beginning *Oct. 1*, **19***86*, **and ending on** *Sept. 30*, **19***88*. **The total rent for this term is** *seven thousand two hundred* **Dollars ($** *7200* **). Said rent shall be due and payable to the Realtor in** *24* **equal monthly installments of** *three hundred* **Dollars ($** *300* **). Payment is to be made on the first day of each month in advance.**

WORDS AND MEANINGS

legally binding contracts—a contract is an agreement, usually a written agreement. When it is "legally binding," it means the law and courts can force people to do what they have agreed to.

lessor—the landlord, the owner

lessee—the person renting, the tenant

realtor—person or company who manages property for a landlord

let—rent

term—the period of time that the lease is in effect

installment—payment. "In 24 equal monthly installments" means the same amount of rent is paid every month. The total of the 24 payments equals the rent for the entire term of the lease.

payment in advance—payment before you use something

QUESTIONS

1. Match—

__ Max Ryle	a. landlord
__ Ginia Sands	b. manager for landlord
Western Management	c. tenant

2. How much is Ginia's monthly rent?

   $__________

3. When is Ginia expected to pay the rent for July?

   __ a. by July 1

   __ b. by July 31

4. How many years is the term of the lease?

   ____

5. Ginia is expected to make her monthly payments to —

   __ a. Max Ryle

   __ b. Western Management

35. LEASE—Part

Below is more of Ginia's lease.

<u>Security Deposit</u>

Lessee shall deposit with the Realtor the amount of *three hundred* Dollars ($ *300*) as security for the full performance by Lessee of all conditions of this Lease. In the event that Lessee does not live up to any conditions of the Lease, then Realtor shall have the right to use and retain any part of the security as necessary to correct the problems caused by Lessee's failure. If Lessee performs all conditions of the Lease fully and satisfactorily and after expiration of Lease and surrender of possession of property in clean condition and good repair, then Realtor shall return security to Lessee.

<u>Use</u>

Lessee will use said property as *residence for 2 adults*.

<u>Late Fee</u>

If Realtor does not receive full payment of rent on or before the fifth day of the month when it is due, then Lessee will pay a late fee of *ten* Dollars ($ *10*). This late fee will be added to the rent.

WORDS AND MEANINGS

security deposit—extra money that the tenant pays to the landlord or realtor before moving in. The money is for any damage the tenant may do or for any rent the tenant may fail to pay. If all the rent is paid and no damage is done, the tenant should get the security back when she or he moves out.

full performance of all conditions—doing everything that you agree to do in the lease

retain—hold on to

expiration—end

surrender of possession—moving out, turning in the key

residence—place where people live, but do not work

QUESTIONS

1. Before Ginia moved in, she paid the first month's rent plus the security deposit.
   How much in total did this come to?
   $__________

2. Ginia paid January's rent on January 3rd.
   Was there a penalty?
   __ yes   __ no

3. Ginia paid May's rent on May 22nd.
   How much was the penalty?
   $__________

4. When Ginia moved out at the end of her lease, the realtor found she had taken out a door and thrown it away. The realtor had to buy a new door.
   Do you think Ginia got back all of her security deposit?
   __ yes   __ no

5. Ginia moved into the apartment with a roommate.
   Read the section "Use." Does the lease allow Ginia to have a roommate?
   __ yes   __ no

6. The picture above shows a business Ginia wants to set up in her living room.
   Does the lease say she can do this?
   __ yes   __ no

7. Refer again to the section on "Use."
   Does the lease allow Ginia to rent out two rooms of the apartment to four of her friends?
   __ yes   __ no

36. LEASE—Part 3

Below is more of Ginia's lease. Notice how Ginia has taken care of problems that might cause her trouble later. Notice the crossed-out paragraph. When something already written in a lease is changed, everybody who signs the lease initials the change.

Sublet

No part of the property shall be sublet without written consent of Lessor or Realtor.

Inspection

The Lessee has inspected the property and agrees to accept it in its present condition, unless otherwise specified.

Pets

GS. MR. LD for Western Management

~~Pets are not allowed on the property without the written consent of Lessor or Realtor.~~

Alterations

Lessee must make no alterations to the property without the written consent of the Lessor or Realtor.

Defaults

Any violation by Lessee of any of the provisions, covenant, and conditions of this Lease shall be a default. In the event of a default by Lessee, all the rent still due for the entire term of the Lease shall become due and payable immediately.

Special Provisions

Lessor will provide a new refrigerator.

November 1986 and December 1986 shall be rent free in return for a satisfactory job of painting the entire 4 rooms in the apartment.

WORDS AND MEANINGS

sublet—when a tenant rents an apartment or house to someone

consent—agreement. Written consent means what it says.

unless otherwise specified—unless something else is written somewhere in the lease

alterations—changes in an apartment that are difficult or expensive to change back

default—failure to live up to a contract

violation—breaking an agreement

provision, covenant, or condition—points agreed to in the lease

due and payable—means you owe it and have to pay it

QUESTIONS

1. Ginia wants to rent her apartment for six weeks to a couple of friends. She figures the landlord won't mind.

   What is the best advice for Ginia?

   __ a. get it in writing

   __ b. forget it

   __ c. do it now, worry later

2. Read the sections on "Inspection" and "Special Provisions."

   What is "otherwise specified" about the condition of the apartment?

   __ a. nothing—Ginia has to take it as is

   __ b. new refrigerator and two months free rent in return for painting the apartment

3. Ginia has a dog, so she crossed out the section on pets.

   When you cross out anything in a lease, make sure that you put your initials next to the cross-out. And also make sure the other people signing the lease do the same thing. This shows that everyone agrees to the cross-out.

   Did everyone agree to crossing out the section on pets?

   __ yes __ no

4. The section on alterations says that Ginia needs written permission if she wants to make any major changes in the apartment that would be hard to change back.

   Which of the following changes would need the written consent of the landlord or realtor? (Check as many as apply.)

   __ a. hang curtains

   __ b. remove radiator and throw it out

   __ c. take out a wall

   __ d. paint stripes on the ceiling

5. Ginia still has six months to go on her lease. She has found a new apartment she likes better.

   Suppose she just skips out, without notice.

   What is the worst that can happen to her?

   __ a. nothing

   __ b. she can lose one month's rent

   __ c. she can wind up having to pay six month's rent

37. NOTICE TO PAY OR QUIT

The notice below is a serious warning of danger ahead. Eddie and Sheila Howard have not paid their rent. The threatening letter is from the landlord's agent.

WESTERN MANAGEMENT COMPANY
SPECIALIST IN PROPERTY MANAGEMENT
3220 Darren Blvd., Iowa City, Iowa 52244 • Telephone 466-8133

TO: Edward and Sheila Howard
6365 A Hazelip Court
Iowa City, Iowa 52243

TAKE NOTICE that you are justly indebted to Western Management Company in the sum of $ 317.50, for the rent of the following premises, to wit: 6365A Hazelip Court, Iowa City, Iowa 52243, at the monthly rental rate of $ 305.00. Western Management Company hereby requires and demands possession of the aforesaid premises or the payment of said rent within five (5) days after service of this Notice, plus $2.50 cost of service of process of this Notice, by the Sheriff of the County, plus $10.00 late charge. The total amount owed by you is therefore $ 317.50, and you must make payment by cashier's check, certified check, or money order within the time limit indicated above. If you default in this payment Western Management Company shall proceed by due process of law to recover possession and money judgement for rent due by virtue of the lease, plus a reasonable attorney's fee, when authorized by law.

DATED July 15, 1986

BY: Thomas T. Tanner
Thomas T. Tanner
Property Manager
3220 Darren Boulevard
Iowa City, IA 52243

WORDS AND MEANINGS

quit—to leave an apartment, or to be forced out of an apartment

justly indebted—owe

premises—house or apartment

to wit—namely

demands possession of the aforesaid premises—wants the tenant out of the apartment

service of process of this notice—getting this notice to the tenant

cashier's check and **certified check**—special checks you buy from the bank or pay the bank to OK. Not regular personal checks.

money order—another kind of special check. You can buy a money order at the Post Office or at a bank.

default—not paying or not doing something one agreed to

proceed by due process of law—go to court

recover possession—throw the tenant out

money judgement—court order to pay money

by due virtue of the lease—because of the lease

attorney's fee—they will want the tenant to pay for the landlord's lawyer

when authorized by law—if and when the court allows

QUESTIONS

1. What is the total amount the landlord's agent wants now?

   __ $10 __ $305 __ $317.50

2. What is this money for? (Check all but one.)

   __ a. a late charge
   __ b. cost of giving the notice to the Howards
   __ c. cost of the landlord's agent's lawyer
   __ d. the month's rent

3. How long do they have to pay it?

   ____________ days

4. Which one of the following can they use to pay it?

   __ a. a certified check
   __ b. an I.O.U.
   __ c. a regular personal check

5. The landlord's agent threatens to use the courts. If the Howards don't pay, what does the agent want the courts to do to them? (Check all but one.)

   __ a. force them to pay the rent
   __ b. force them out of the apartment
   __ c. force them to pay for the landlord's lawyer
   __ d. force them into jail

6. The Howards feel they don't owe the money. What do you think would be good advice for them?

   __ a. talk to a lawyer soon
   __ b. tell the landlord's agent off
   __ c. wait and see

38. BOOKLET ON PAINTING

The paragraphs below come from a booklet about paint.

CHOOSING COLORS

Color is mostly a matter of personal preference. Remember that light colors will repel heat while dark tones absorb heat.

Paints are available in a wide range of colors and shades. Some are ready mixed; others the dealer has to mix by adding or combining different colors. Dealers usually carry color charts showing the different possibilities. Here are some points to keep in mind in selecting your colors.

• Light colors make a small room seem larger. Conversely, dark colors make an overly large room appear smaller.

• Ceilings appear lower when darker than the walls and higher when lighter than the walls.

• Paint generally dries to a slightly different color or shade.

• Colors often change under artificial lighting. Look at color swatches both in daylight and under artificial lighting.

• The type of artificial lighting can also make a difference. For instance, incandescent lighting casts a warm, yellow glow. On the other hand, fluorescent lighting usually gives off a cooler, blue hue.

• Keep in mind that most paint stores use fluorescent lighting, and consequently a color that looks one shade in the paint store may look another shade in your home. Adjacent colors also affect the appearance.

WORDS AND MEANINGS

personal preference—what you like

repel heat—bounce heat off so it doesn't get very hot

absorb heat—take heat in so it gets hot

shades (of color)—colors that are only slightly different from each other, like the different kinds of blue or the different kinds of red

ready mixed paint—paint mixed in the can, by the paint maker

color charts—sheets with little blocks of color, to show you what color paints you can buy

conversely—on the other hand

artificial lighting—light from light bulbs (instead of sunlight)

swatches—little samples showing paint color. Similiar to color charts.

incandescent—light from light bulbs with wires that glow inside, common in homes

fluorescent—light from tubes coated on the inside with a material that glows, common in offices and stores

consequently—as a result; therefore

adjacent—nearby

QUESTIONS

1. Drake wants to make the ceiling look higher. He painted the walls brown. He is thinking of black or white for the ceiling. Which one should he choose?
   __ a. black
   __ b. white

2. The floor in Drake's apartment gets a lot of sun. Which color will make it feel the hottest to bare feet?
   __ a. white
   __ b. light gray
   __ c. black

3. Which is an incandescent light?

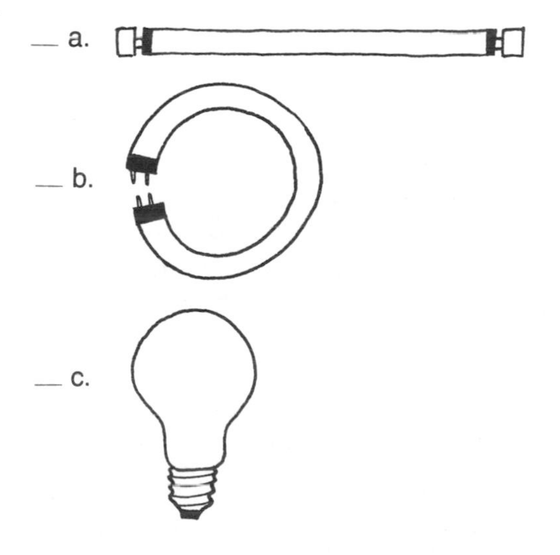

   __ a.
   __ b.
   __ c.

4. What is the most likely mistake made by the man in the picture?

   __ a. he picked too light a color
   __ b. he picked too dark a color
   __ c. he painted it when it was too hot

5. This article is mainly about —
   __ a. how paint companies make paint
   __ b. the history of paint
   __ c. things to think about when you pick out paint colors

6. The article says that different kinds of light can —
   __ a. cause a fire
   __ b. make the color of paint look different
   __ c. ruin the paint

39. GUARANTEE OR WARRANTY

Sanders Products, Inc., gives out the warranty shown below every time someone buys one of its appliances.

SANDERS PRODUCTS, INC.

FULL ONE-YEAR WARRANTY

Sanders Products, Inc., warrants that this appliance shall be free from defects in material and workmanship for a period of one year from the date of purchase. This warranty does not cover consequential damages of any kind or wear resulting from accident, misuse, abuse, commercial use or breakage of glass (if applicable).

If your appliance fails to operate properly while in use under normal household conditions within the warranty period, simply send or return the complete appliance prepaid to Sanders Service Center or any Sanders factory authorized service station. If the appliance is found by Sanders to be defective in material or workmanship, Sanders will repair or replace it free of charge. If you are sending your appliance, please include a memo giving your name and address, the model number, reason for return, date purchased, and where purchased. Please allow three to four weeks for mailing and servicing time.

IMPORTANT: Be sure to return all parts with the appliance, pack carefully, and indicate your return address on the outside of the package. You may wish to insure the package against possible damage or loss in transit.

WORDS AND MEANINGS

guarantee or warranty—a promise to fix or replace something you buy if it doesn't work

appliance—a piece of equipment you use around your house, such as an electric fan or a stove

defects—faults

consequential damages—see Lesson 12, Questions 10-12

misuse—not using something correctly

abuse—harming something

commercial use—using something to make money from customers

prepaid—paid ahead of time. Here it is talking about postage or shipping.

factory authorized service stations—places the company has chosen to fix its products

memo—written note

in transit—in the mail, or while being shipped

QUESTIONS

1. Match–

__ defects in materials and workmanship	A. Sanders pays
__ accident, misuse, abuse, commercial use, breakage of glass	B. you pay

2. You buy a Sanders blender in October 1985. It stops working in March 1987.

   Is it still covered by the warranty?

   __ yes __ no

3. Your Sanders blender won't work. It is still under warranty, and the problem is the fault of Sanders.

   Who pays the shipping charge when you send it to the Service Center?

   __ a. Sanders does

   __ b. you do

4. Who decides if Sanders is responsible for fixing your blender free of charge?

   __ a. Sanders does

   __ b. you do

5. In which case(s) will Sanders probably fix the appliance free of charge? (Check one or more. Note that all of the problems below occur within the warranty period.)

   __ a. Laverne takes good care of her blender, but the motor stopped

   __ b. Osella got mad and threw her blender across the kitchen—it broke

   __ c. Rea takes good care of her mixer, too, but the glass bowl broke

40. OWNER'S MANUAL FOR A FIRE EXTINGUISHER

Below is part of the Operating Instructions from the Owner's Manual for a fire extinguisher. Read it carefully, and look at the drawings showing the parts of the extinguisher.

OWNER'S MANUAL for FIRE EXTINGUISHER

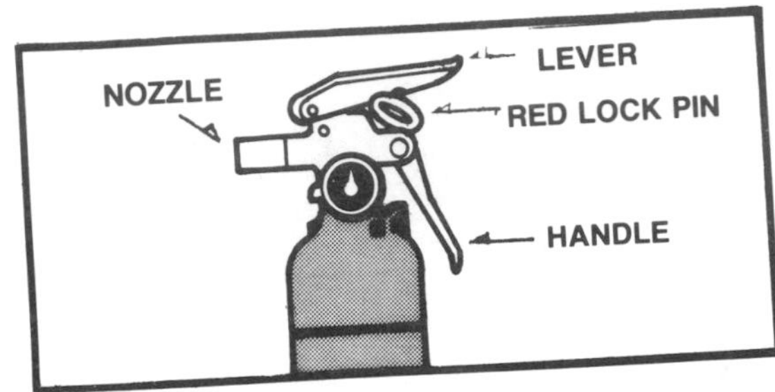

OPERATING INSTRUCTIONS

Remove from wall hanger or strap/clamp bracket.

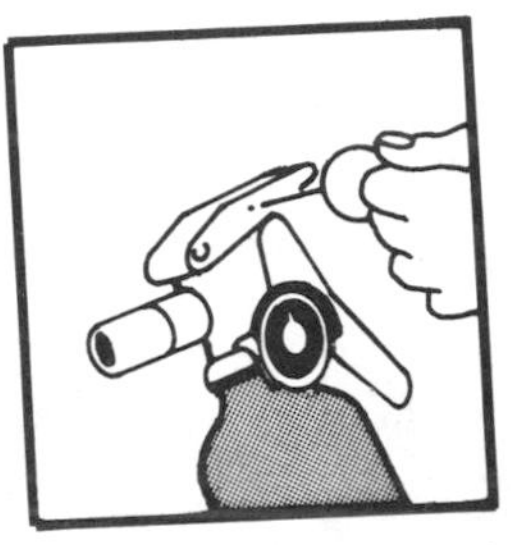

Grasp unit and pull red lock pin from lever and handle. Hold unit upright with hand under handle and thumb on top of lever. Unit is designed to discharge the dry chemical agent ONLY IN UPRIGHT POSITION.

Keep safe distance from fire (at least 6 feet) and near an exit. Aim nozzle at base of fire (not at flames or smoke). Do not get too close as the discharge stream may scatter the fire. If it does, move back. Play it safe. Keep away from the fire's fuel source and avoid breathing vapors, fumes and heated smoke as much as possible.

Press lever downward and spray dry chemical powder (powder stream will shoot over 10 foot distance) at base of flame in quick, side-to-side motion to erase the flames. When the extinguishing agent comes in contact with the fire, the fire will flare and appear to grow larger. Don't panic. This condition is a normal and temporary reaction before the agent suppresses the fire. Direct all of the discharging dry chemical agent on the fire and make sure the fire is completely extinguished. After fire is out, carefully watch for "flashback".

WORDS AND MEANINGS

fire extinguisher—a thing you use to spray chemicals that put out fires

grasp—hold on to

lock pin—a special red-colored pin that runs through the lever on top of the extinguisher. The extinguisher only works when you pull the lock pin out.

lever—thing you push down to make the extinguisher work

chemical agent—the special chemicals that do the job of putting out the fire

discharge—send out

nozzle—the "nose" of the extinguisher, where the chemical agent sprays out of

vapors and fumes—gases

erase—get rid of

flare—suddenly get bigger

panic—do crazy things when you suddenly feel a lot of fear

suppresses—puts out

extinguished—put out

QUESTIONS

1. Georgia quickly took the extinguisher from the wall, hurried to the fire, and pushed the lever. Nothing happened.

   What was probably wrong?

   __ a. she forgot to uncover the nozzle

   __ b. she forgot to refill the chemical

   __ c. she forgot to unlock the lever

2. Look at this picture:

   Which arrow shows where you aim the nozzle?

   __ arrow A __ arrow B

3. What is a good distance to stand when you put out a fire with this extinguisher?

   __ a. 1 to 5 feet from the fire

   __ b. 6 to 10 feet from the fire

   __ c. 10 to 20 feet from the fire

4. What should you do if the force of the chemical hitting the fire seems to be spreading the fire around?

   __ a. move closer

   __ b. move back

   __ c. turn down the amount of chemical

5. People putting out fires with this extinguisher are often frightened because when the chemical first hits the fire it ______________.

   (fill in the word)

6. The word flashback as used in the Operating Instructions (last word) probably means—

   __ a. fire coming back to life after being put out

   __ b. remembering something from the past

   __ c. sparks flying as the fire burns

41. CAMERA FILM INSTRUCTIONS

This card is the protective cover on a film pack of instant-picture color film.

THIS COVER PROTECTS YOUR FILM, DO NOT REMOVE.

For better daylight pictures of people...

1. Stand so the light falling on the subject comes from behind you or from the side.

2. Watch the background; it should be fairly evenly lit and have about the same brightness as the subject.

3. Move in close; make your subject fill the picture area.

4. Squeeze the shutter button and hold the camera steady until the picture is ejected. Any camera movement while the shutter is open will produce a blurred picture.

← HOLD ONLY BY SIDES →
DON'T SQUEEZE THIS END

WORDS AND MEANINGS

subject—person or thing you are taking a picture of

background—anything behind the subject that will also be in the picture

shutter—part of a camera that opens and closes very fast to let light in for a very short time. This light takes the picture.

shutter button—button that you press to operate the shutter and take the picture

ejected—pushed out

blurred—fuzzy-looking, not sharp

QUESTIONS

1. What do the instructions tell you to do with this film pack cover?
   __ a. take if off and throw it away
   __ b. keep it on the film pack
   __ c. take it off and turn it over, then put it back

2. How are you supposed to hold the pack of film when you drop it into the camera?
   __ a. hold gently, by the sides
   __ b. hold firmly at the ends

3. These directions tell you how to take pictures with light from—
   __ a. flash bulbs
   __ b. light bulbs
   __ c. the sun

4. Judy wants to take a picture of her sister, who is wearing a bright yellow jump suit. Judy poses her sister in bright light, against a dark background of pine trees in deep shadow.
   Will this probably make a good picture?
   __ yes __ no

5. Which will probably give you a bad picture?
   __ a. light on the front of the subject's face
   __ b. light on the side of the subject's face
   __ c. light coming from behind the subject

6. How do you get the picture out of the camera?
   a. open the back and take it out
   __ b. it comes out automatically
   __ c. send the camera to the manufacturer

7. The subject in your picture looks too small. What's probably wrong?
   __ a. you used the wrong size film
   __ b. you photographed a small person
   __ c. you were too far away from the subject when you took the picture

8. Your pictures come out fuzzy. What's probably wrong?
   __ a. the film was crooked
   __ b. you didn't have enough light
   __ c. you moved when the shutter was open

42. SAFETY NOTICE

This is a safety notice sent by a gas company to its customers.

IF YOU SMELL GAS

If you notice an odor of gas either indoors or outdoors, call our emergency service right away—**643-4050.** When you need our emergency service, remember these DO'S and DON'Ts:

Open windows in the area where you smell the odor. Breathing natural gas will not harm you if there is sufficient air to breathe along with it.

• Call 643-4050. • Wait for our emergency serviceperson to arrive. • Do not light matches. • Do not turn on an electric light or do anything that might create a spark.

Please don't misuse the fast service we provide for emergency calls. Reporting an odor of gas just to get a faster response to a routine service call is irresponsible and unfair to those who actually need emergency service quickly. For this reason, servicepersons responding to emergency calls will provide emergency service **only!**

WORDS AND MEANINGS

odor—a smell

emergency service—repair persons who will help in a hurry when there's danger

natural gas—the kind of gas piped into homes for heating and for cooking stoves

sufficient—enough

misuse—use badly or use wrongly

response—an answer or an action in answer to something

irresponsible—not fair, not doing what you should do

provide—give

QUESTIONS

1. You walk into a dark room at night. The smell of gas is very strong. What should you do?
   __ a. get out immediately
   __ b. open windows
   __ c. strike a match

2. How harmful is breathing natural gas?
   __ a. very hamful—the smell means an amount in the air that will make you sick
   __ b. not harmful if you have enough air with it
   __ c. not harmful at all, ever

3. The burners in Frank's gas stove don't work well, so he called the emergency service. What does the notice say that the service people will do when they come?
   __ a. fix his stove
   __ b. leave without fixing the stove
   __ c. check for gas leaks

4. The notice says,

   "Reporting an odor of gas just to get a faster response to a routine service call is irresponsible and unfair."

   What do you think the word <u>routine</u> means in this context?
   __ a. emergency
   __ b. bad-smelling
   __ c. ordinary, regular

5. Jeanne smelled a strong odor of gas in her dark kitchen. She switched on a light, and there was an explosion.

   What does the paragraph say is probably the reason for this?
   __ a. darkness causes gas to explode by itself
   __ b. the brightness of the light causes gas to explode by itself
   __ c. a spark in the light switch causes gas to explode

43. PUBLIC HEALTH NOTICE

The notice below is from the City Department of Health. It is posted on the bulletin board outside several neighborhood grocery stores and supermarkets.

MEASLES ALERT

Measles cases have been reported in your neighborhood.

Measles is one of the most serious childhood diseases. It can cause pneumonia, blindness, inflammation of the brain, and deafness. *Measles* is most frequent in young children over six months of age, but it also occurs frequently in teenagers and young adults. *Measles* lasts about two weeks, beginning with symptoms like those of a bad cold: fever, irritated eyes, dry cough, and a runny nose. These symptoms are followed by a blotchy red rash which lasts from seven to ten days.

You and your family may have been exposed to this disease. Make sure you are protected:

A person who has had measles disease (diagnosed by a doctor) is immune and will not get the disease again.

A person who received live attenuated vaccine after the age of a year is immune and will not get the disease.

A child who received measles vaccine before the age of one year should get a second dose to be adequately protected.

Any person who has not had measles disease and is not adequately immunized should consult their health care provider as soon as possible for preventive care.

If a member of your family develops measles please notify the City Immunization Office for assistance and follow-up.
Call 427-1940.

WORDS AND MEANINGS

alert—a warning to be on the lookout for something dangerous

disease—a sickness

pneumonia—a serious lung disease

inflammation—swelling and pain caused by disease

symptoms—signs of disease

irritated—sore

blotchy red rash—skin covered with red spots that are irregular in shape, not round and neat

exposed to this disease—people with this disease have been near you, and you may catch it

diagnosed by a doctor—a doctor has said you have this disease

immune—cannot get the disease

attenuated—weakened

vaccine—a mixture containing killed or weakened disease germs, given to people to make them immune to the disease. When people are given a vaccine, they are said to be **vaccinated** or **immunized.**

consult—get advice or help

health care provider—doctor or nurse

QUESTIONS

1. Why did the city put up this notice?
   __ a. because of a health problem
   __ b. because of a plan to make the neighborhood prettier
   __ c. because too many children were staying out of school

2. According to the notice, how serious a disease is measles?
   __ a. not serious at all
   __ b. very serious

3. Which of the following people needs measles vaccine?
   __ a. Benny, age 7, was vaccinated once when 9 months old
   __ b. Raquel, age 4, was vaccinated at age 2
   __ c. Mr. Delgado, age 60, had measles as a child

4. Which of the following has symptoms of measles?
   __ a. Nancy: light hurts her eyes. She has a high temperature and red spots on her skin
   b. Eric: he has pains in his stomach, feels like throwing up, and his muscles hurt.
   __ c. Vicky: she has a sore throat and large swelling in her neck

5. Liza Gillis gets measles. What does the notice tell her to do?
   __ a. do nothing—it's too late
   __ b. get vaccinated
   __ c. call 427-1940